Monograph Series of the
Boston Psychoanalytic Society and Institute, No. 1

The

Psychosomatic Concept
in Psychoanalysis

EDITED BY FELIX DEUTSCH, M.D.

—

INTERNATIONAL UNIVERSITIES PRESS, INC.

New York

CONTENTS

v

PREFACE

The Program Committee[1] of the Boston Psychoanalytic Society and Institute was moved to conduct a symposium on psychosomatic medicine by the very fact that many psychoanalysts have raised various questions in regard to the scientific status of the psychosomatic concept within the framework of psychoanalysis.

The purpose of this symposium was to present a unit of five lectures which should cover the current trends of this concept. It proposed five topics for the discussion:

1. Genetic and Dynamic Psychophysiological Determinants of Pathophysiological Processes
2. Some Current Trends and Hypotheses of Psychosomatic Research
3. The Problem of Specificity in the Psychosomatic Process
4. Genesis of Psychosomatic Symptoms in Infancy
5. Problems in Therapy

At the conclusion of the lecture series, a discussion followed which highlighted and further clarified some of the pertinent questions raised in these papers. For that reason, it was decided to include it in the monograph. Not all the problems in regard to the status of psychosomatic medicine within psychoanalysis appear to be touched upon in these lectures. However, the essential points were stressed, indicating the direction

[1] Bernard Bandler, M.D., Felix Deutsch, M.D., and Gregory Rochlin, M.D., were members of the Program Committee.

which future clinical work and experimental research should take.

The Committee feels indebted to Dr. A. S. Kagan, the publisher, for his interest in this symposium. We also wish to acknowledge the valuable assistance and helpful suggestions received throughout the preparation of this book from Miss Lottie Maury, editor of International Universities Press.

FELIX DEUTSCH, M.D.

THE PSYCHOSOMATIC CONCEPT
IN PSYCHOANALYSIS

INTRODUCTION

The Psychosomatic Concept in Psychoanalysis
Symposium held on February 9-10th, 1952

Dr. Felix Deutsch:

It is my privilege to welcome today the guest speakers
of this symposium, who accepted the invitation to contribute to the clarification of the psychosomatic concept
in psychoanalysis.

This "concept" covers more than what is called "psychosomatic medicine." It seems as if the word "medicine" had been a stumbling block against the implementation of this concept into analytical thinking. In other
words, what is open for discussion today are not disease
entities which are brought together from the medical
point of view, but elements of psychophysiological
functions which begin with fetal life, and which continually remain active during normal psychic and biologic development throughout life. For this reason, it is
not the problem of psychogenesis which has to be dealt
with. It is to be expected that the central core of the
discussion will be the problem of "the specificity of the
psychosomatic process" and of "the choice of the organ."
The contents of the papers may be overlapping, but will
represent a closed unit.

1

GENETIC AND DYNAMIC PSYCHO-PHYSIOLOGICAL DETERMINANTS OF PATHOPHYSIOLOGICAL PROCESSES

SYDNEY G. MARGOLIN, M. D.[1]

The invitation to participate in this symposium was extended in the form of a challenge. The topics and problems were assigned with the expectation that final answers and solutions could not and would not be offered by the contributors. It was hoped that the boundaries of our knowledge would be indicated and that the direction of our speculations and operational hypotheses would be frankly expressed. In short, I was asked to provide samplings of conceptual thinking and of work in progress.

The general subject of the "Metapsychology of Psychosomatic Symptom Formation" was offered to me. I chose to see this problem in the light of current psychoanalytic theory; that is, in terms of ego psychology. Hence the more specific title of my essay is the "Genetic and Dynamic Psychophysiological Determinants of Pathophysiological Processes."[2]

[1] Associate Psychiatrist, The Mount Sinai Hospital, New York City; New York Psychoanalytic Society; President, American Psychosomatic Society, 1952-1953.

[2] This paper is an extended report of material previously submitted before the Group for the Advancement of Psychiatry. It was privately circularized in 1947 in Circular Letter No. 114.

At the outset, I shall make certain declarations which will indicate to some extent the methodological positions in the biological, psychological, and social fields from which I speak.

1. I do not believe in "psychogenesis"; that is, that a psychophysiological process is initiated *de novo* in the mind. Mental events in both health and disease are but links in the psychosomatic chain of events (Deutsch, 2; Margolin, 11). The postulation of circular and reverberating circuits in the brain (Kubie, 8; McCulloch, 15) which can trigger off random or stereotyped effector responses does not contradict this point of view. Such circuits have historical determinants derived from experience and serve to increase the latent period preceding a given response. Even when an irritable focus is present as in organic brain disease, the principle of stimulus and response still applies. In short, a structural, functional continuum exists between the mind and the environment (including the body) which contains nodal points at which occur transformations of energy.

2. I do not believe in psychosomatic medicine as the diagnosis and treatment of a special class of sharply defined clinical entities such as ulcerative colitis or asthma. As will be discussed later, these are syndromes which have a variety of pathogenic mechanisms. Accordingly, profile and specificity of conflict concepts could not be fruitfully used.

3. Because of these considerations, I have turned more and more to the investigation of psychophysiological mechanisms as they occur in healthy and sick people. From a somatic point of view, organs, tissues and their functions are studied rather than an arbitrary

collection of signs and symptoms designating a disease. For example, the problem of obesity can be formulated in terms of a metabolic substance (adrenal cortical steroids) which can augment the psychic representation of hunger, i.e., appetite. Such steroids would then be part of the somatic complex of the oral instinct (Margolin, 12).

Moods, affects and emotions are dealt with as psychophysiological states which have varying degrees and kinds of compatibility with the pathophysiological processes of any given disease. Operationally, such a concept may contribute to systematic rational therapy of disease.

4. The ultimate test of methodology in psychosomatic research must be based on whether our knowledge of bodily and mental mechanisms can be advanced both in theory and practice.

Psychosomatic medicine is regarded in several ways. Viewed idealistically, all bodily states in health and disease are psychosomatic in that a psychological factor of varying intensity is present. Practically, however, it has become customary to apply this term to a group of diverse clinical entities such as asthma, ulcerative colitis, hypertension, neurodermatitis, duodenal ulcer and a host of functional disturbances without fixed anatomic pathology (Margolin and Kaufman, 14). These illnesses have in common the fact of psychological features which appear to be significant as etiological factors. Both the diseases and the mental aspects are classified in various ways according to the systematization of human psychology to which the investigator subscribes and according to his concept by which mental processes

5

are mediated to the organ that manifests the patho-physiology (MacCleod, Wittkower, and Margolin, 10).

Many textbooks beginning with Dunbar (4) which attempt to deal with the subject as a whole, tend to classify psychosomatic diseases by the organ systems. This is in the tradition of classical anatomy, physiology and pathology. Thus we read of "Diseases of the Gastro-Intestinal Tract," of the "Cardio-Respiratory System," of the "Skin and Its Appendages"—and so forth. Many monographs have been written on the diseases of individual systems, and on diseases of organs as parts of systems.

The defect of this nosological system is that it is unrelated to considerations of the role of such psychophysiological phenomena as emotions, affects and moods. Moreover, in bodily disease only organs or parts of organs are involved in the anatomical and functional disturbance, rarely, if ever, entire organ systems. Secondly, an organ system which contains diverse tissues and functions, must be under some form of central regulatory control, if coördinated and adaptive behavior is to take place. From a psychological point of view, only those functions of an organ or of its constituent tissues which have been experienced have central representation. In other words, both such a system of classification of psychosomatic medicine and its taxonomic principles are not psychophysiological.

The following is an effort to apply these considerations to a nosology of psychosomatic diseases. The majority of psychosomatic disturbances as observed clinically and experimentally appear to have at least two phases. The first is functional and consists of reversible

6

disproportionate or inappropriate motor, secretory and vascular responses in an organ or in its constituent tissues; e.g., hyperfunction, hypofunction, perversion of function, and synchrony or asynchrony. These can be readily observed in the musculoskeletal system, in respiration, anal and urinary sphincters, ingestion of food and in the organs of special sensation. The second phase is the establishment of fixed tissue changes which may be reversible in the sense of the body economy but which invariably leaves an altered tissue state, such as the ligamentous and articular alterations in conversion hysteria, deformity of duodenal cap in ulcer, mucosal hyperplasia in ulcerative colitis, and changes in the thoracic cage and pulmonary tissue in asthma. During this phase, the mechanisms of the preceding functional phase often continue but may be obscured or distorted by the effects of the tissue pathology and by the systemic reactions to them, such as fever, anorexia and loss of weight. Moreover, the second phase introduces a new bodily situation to which secondary and reactive psychic responses develop and to which the psychophysiological economy must adapt. It should be emphasized that the two phases differ in symptoms, pathophysiology, clinical signs, diagnosis, prognosis and therapy. Where such a host of quantitative and qualitative differential features occur, two different but interrelated diseases must be considered. This distinction is of fundamental importance if the effects of therapy are to be evaluated and compared.

There are certain genetic and developmental aspects of the first or functional phase which on reflection appear to be of the greatest relevance. A convenient and

perhaps oversimplified way of regarding these physiological factors is in terms of the principle of homeostasis. In the newborn infant the nodal points at which
compensatory restitutive mechanisms are called into
play are widely separated; that is, respiration, pulse
rate, pulmonary oxygen tension, fluid and caloric intake
tend to be highly irregular. In other words, processes
are reversible at relatively extreme degrees of fluctuation and thresholds are high at which the reversal is
initiated. In terms of the two-phase concept, irreversible
tissue changes in infancy do not occur as readily as they
do in adults. For example, the neonate appears to toler-
ate without damage relatively high degrees of anoxia,
severe depletion of fluid and electrolyte reserves,
marked shifts in body temperature, pulse rate, cardiac
output, pulmonary ventilation and nutritional requirements. To put this situation somewhat schematically,
the graphic picture of the ontogenesis of homeostatic
boundaries is a funnel-shaped affair. It is widest at
birth, contracts rapidly with age to relatively narrow
ranges for most bodily variables. This is determined by
such factors as changes in the resilience of blood vessels,
postnatal maturation of endocrines, and specific metabolic processes of nervous tissues which are more ex-
quisitely dependent on physiologic constancy and more
sensitive to pathophysiological stresses. The capacity
for adaptation is further conditioned by infections,
trauma and, of course, the big unknown, constitution,
such as, for example, an inherently determined rate of
developmental change of structure and function. With
maturation, there is a shift from local autonomous organ
behavior and reflexes toward centralization and co-

ördination by means of the central nervous system. The mass reactions of the newborn are gradually transformed into selected patterns which are more economically related to resolving bodily needs.

This process of a change from local tissue autonomy to organized central regulation parallels the infant's development in relation to his environment. At birth, the environment exercises many of the functions which are later assumed by the activities of central regulation. The environment perceives and differentiates the infant's various needs and attempts to fulfill them appropriately and in proportion. The individuals who function in this way serve as the baby's sensory modalities, and as his integrative and executive apparatus; i.e., as a model of the evolving ego which will become apparent later. They strive constantly to restore his psychophysiological equilibrium by maintaining an intuitively and empathically perceived center within his various homeostatic boundaries. In a sense, one can call the infant's tolerance for wide fluctuations in bodily processes a protective mechanism. It compensates for any defects in the sensorial and restitutive responses in the environment. There is much to suggest that such defects are subsequently incorporated by the infant's ego. The nodal point for the infant's reflex reaction to internal stresses is close to this hypothetical center and is manifested by psychomotor activity such as crying. Beyond this, and at a considerable distance, is a second nodal point at which the reversibility of vital processes is threatened. This latter point tends to be biologically limited and must always be biologically gratified. The first or alarm-crying point can be influenced by the consistency of the response of the environment. An extreme example of this is the anaclitic depression following chronic neglect of the initial signal and of adequate gratification. The infant cries without relation to his bodily needs or is apathetic to them (Spitz, *18*). In other words, the psychophysiological manifestation of tension, the prototype of anxiety, becomes dissociated from the appropriate means of restoring equilibrium. It is this feature which distinguishes anxiousness (rational fear) from anxiety (irrational fear).

In the neonate, according to these considerations the initial developmental phase is characterized by a basic unity or continuum between it and its environment. There is at best an amorphous ego boundary (Federn, 5); structurally, between id and ego; topologically, between conscious and unconscious; and somatically, between involuntary and voluntary functions. The environment operates for the infant as though it were an involuntary organ in its body. It provides nutrition in the same sense that the liver furnishes glucose. It regulates the ambient temperature to correct for the uncoördinated body heat production or loss. The baby's hunger cry which activates his mother to nurse him acts like an internal humoral stimulus which initiates an internal restitution. To the extent that psychoanalysis has a theory of affects, it is in this early stage that the primary affects of tension (disequilibrium) and gratification (equilibrium) become manifest. This somatic conception of the ego boundary for organ function enters into the psychophysiological adaptation of patients who in later life become aware of previously unconscious bodily functions. This occurs in diabetes, hor-

10

monal replacement therapy, and as a reaction to fistulous openings into the gastrointestinal tract (Margolin, 13). Marked regressive attitudes of varying duration result from these special narcissistic insults (*vide infra*).

Definitely, this is an involuntary psychophysiological phase. That is to say, the infant has no purposeful control of either his bodily or of his environmental functions. In this phase, equilibrium is sleep, disequilibrium is psychomotor activity; and pathological equilibrium is apathy and indifference to gratification as in the anaclitic depression. It should be emphasized that this phase is not static and that this representation is from the point of view of the initial state of the newborn and of the corresponding environmental reaction. In general, the environment tends to resist developmental change in the infant in various ways. The most common is a delay in recognizing the infant's changing needs in terms of frequency of feedings, calorie and fluid intake, sleeping patterns in relation to gratification, emergence of new needs based on myelinization, muscular coördination and developing sensory modalities.

In addition to resistance to developmental advance in the infant, there is the failure to interpret a psychophysiological regression during teething, infections and trauma. The regression generally consists of resuming feeding and sleeping patterns previously given up. In addition, the viscera appear to become intolerant again to new foods. The baby appears to lose some of the increased capacity for isolation and play which it had acquired. It is as though the infant temporarily retreats to a psychophysiological state with its tried and tested

11

gratifications before assuming the hitherto not yet experienced satisfactions of the next stage. This is understandably induced by the fact that the new development (i.e., advancing maturation) does begin with bodily tension and instability such as danger of falling and trauma. Moreover, each development suddenly confronts the infant with the fact of increasing separation; e.g., crawling and walking physically transport the baby temporarily away from mother. He suddenly discovers that he is taking the initiative in this separation, that is, of weaning himself. This new ego boundary reactivates the original enforced weaning anxiety. The infant attempts to cope with this by means of psychophysiological regression. It is as though he attempts to touch his home base before taking off in the new developmental direction. Needless to say, these regressions should be recognized, tolerated and supported. They are self-limited. If the infant finds his home base available and waiting, it will not be necessary to continue the regressive retreat until a reluctant environment is compelled to acknowledge his difficulties. Prolonging the regression by opposition delays the advance and sets up a pattern of reactive anxiety to progressive change; in short, an anxious "unweaned" child. He becomes predisposed to psychophysiological reactions of avoidance and rejection; e.g., vomiting, diarrhea, abdominal pain, clumsiness, enuresis, encopresis, as well as to autistic psychomotor behavior.

If for any reason the infant is born with certain constitutional limitations such as allergy, rapid oscillation between regression and advance occurs. The failure to accede to the regression sets up either premature weaning or reinforces the weaning trauma. Such traumatic events become psychosomatic nests for subsequent disease and instability.

The baby's reactions to the modes of satisfying its immediate and developing needs can be described as molecular weaning experiences. These become expressions of the larval ego, or more accurately, the first manifestations of ego boundaries. The latter can only appear as a result of the confluence of psychophysiological developments within the baby and of environmental conditions.

One outstanding characteristic of this phase is the uniformity of psychomotor responses to a large variety of disparate and unrelated stimuli. The development of the capacity to discriminate and differentiate stimuli and responses on the one hand, and needs and gratifications on the other, is a function of central integration by the nervous system. There is the familiar situation of the stereotyped repetitive behavior of the compulsion neuroses in which various stimuli are incapable of being differentiated by the patient.

With sensorimotor development, together with the rudimentary ego boundary, purposeful behavior becomes manifest usually in the forms of delaying the postprandial sleep and of temporarily withholding the psychomotor or crying reactions to disequilibria. The infant uses his motor and sensory system both as an independent means of pleasure seeking (gratifying of subinstincts) and as a defense against the disadvantages of deferring the gratification of other instinctual needs. The hungry infant, for example, can be temporarily distracted by sights and sounds so that crying stops. It is as though the hypothetical physiological state called hunger had disappeared. What began as a competition between two modes of pleasure seeking, became each a defense against the other. Eating, the functional phase, and obesity, the tissue phase, become defenses against unacceptable body sensations which were originally pleasurable. To illustrate how far we must go in our biological knowledge, I referred to hunger as a hypothetical tissue state, as distinguished from appetite, a psychic state about which we know a great deal in psychoanalytic terms. The fact is that we do not have an adequate physiological definition of hunger (Janowitz and Grossman, 7). No secretory and motor activities of the stomach, no chemical changes in the blood, in short, no bodily change has been consistently isolated or described which corresponds to the subjective sensation of hunger. The same is true for thirst. The ultimate clarification of the psychophysiological consequences of the oral phase of development awaits such knowledge. Similarly, we have very meager information about defeca-tion, micturition and states of sexual excitement.

Among the bodily structures to come under this gradually developing but slowly controlled and increasing capacity for deferred gratification are the special sense organs, the striated musculoskeletal system and the voluntary components of respiration and of the sphincters dealing with defecation and urination. These structures mature at different rates although they can function serviceably quite early. For example, the infant can walk and possibly accelerate as in running, but the final development of reflex associated motor movements do not begin to appear until the third year. It is at this time that the

14

infant becomes capable of motility and of exerting force which is quantitatively appropriate for the task at hand. Similarly, he can be taught to contract his anal sphincters adaptively, thus inducing motor inhibition of the colon. This will result in a deferment of defecation and the infant will be apparently bowel trained. Before this stage, however, the stimuli which are intended to be specifically appropriate for this behavior are not readily differentiated by the baby. As a result, this response not infrequently becomes conditionally associated with unrelated stimuli, usually arising out of anxiety-charged situations. Such maladaptive anal contraction and colonic inhibition very probably becomes the infantile basis for spastic constipation and abdominal distention. Again the confluence of biological development and environmental participation is apparent. This voluntary control may be precociously induced, or unduly deferred.

Other interesting examples of improperly timed environmental influence are curious vestigial remnants of the infantile gait and posture superimposed on the normal associated movements. There are individuals who walk with forearms slightly flexed, loose dangling hands, arms slightly adducted, thighs adducted and shoulders swinging. This gait is culturally associated with effeminacy. Others walk and move with a kind of impulsive clumsiness, as though they needed a great deal of room. They are slightly flexed at the hips, walk with a swinging gait, with partly flexed forearms swinging out. They give the impression of concentrated hurry. These are examples of retained infantile postural and motility patterns which may follow premature pressure to walk

15

when postural and gait reflexes are not adequately developed or as a regressive reaction to too prolonged inhibition of voluntary control.

Of significance for the thesis of this paper, is the fact that between the total involuntary non-ego functional state of the newborn and the relatively matured purposeful state of the three-year-old, are those structures and functions which have both voluntary and involuntary innervation. These are the organs serving respiration, defecation and urination and musculoskeletal activities which by training and experience become automatic, stereotyped and skilled. It should be pointed out at this place that true sphincter control and controlled speech do not usually occur without the kind of maturation of the voluntary nervous system just described. It is only then that the child and his parent have real confidence in his ability to avoid soiling and wetting himself. Control which is achieved before this is frequently uneconomic, unreliable and associated with an undue effort to concentrate on the significance of bodily stimuli arising within the abdomen, especially in the bladder and bowel. The means of control become more important than the purposes for which control is necessary (a perversion of emphasis which is characteristic of compulsive neuroses).

Physiologically both regressive incontinence and "false alarms" are observed; i.e., an apparent desire to void or defecate without results or the counterpart, impulsive bladder and bowel urgency. An important clinical variant of this aspect, which is associated with some forms of frigidity in women and of orgastic dissatisfaction in men, exists in those individuals who appear to be unable to interpret sensations from their excretory viscera. They frequently present themselves to physicians with the complaint of a dysfunction of urination or defecation. In order to avoid sensations from the bladder and colon, they attempt to void and defecate by the clock without regard to bodily needs for this relief. Associated with this are anxieties and inhibitions having to do with being observed while performing these functions.

When sexual functions are involved, the tensions leading to orgasm are suppressed and, so to speak, there are no sexual tensions to discharge. There is an oral type of this conflict which is displaced upward and results both in obesity and in postprandial vomiting. The subjective sensations of hunger and satiety are avoided and hence not experienced. The distention of overeating is relieved by induced vomiting which does not inhibit the resumption of eating. The regulation of physiological nutrition becomes conscious to the greatest possible degree and normal bodily signals are avoided. Another clinical example involves defecation in which the patient was compelled to reach up into his anus for his own feces. He preferred the voluntary manual removal to involuntary evacuation.

Behind the exaggeratedly controlled voluntary behavior in these patients is the repetition compulsion to master an anxiety which in the deeper sense is related to an archaic weaning, or separation reaction. The bodily sensations indicate an unacceptable state of disequilibrium which the individual must correct by himself. The compulsion serves to reënact an infantile unity with the mother in which these various functions are regulated as though under her external command. Ex-

17

ceptional preoccupation with suicide, dying and death wishes occur with great frequency in such patients. They experience intense somatic distress when compelled to give up this effort at visceral anesthesia.

To summarize, the psychosomatic, developmental process in the infant can be divided into three phases according to the state of internal central regulation. These are the initial involuntary, the combined involuntary-voluntary, and the voluntary phases. All three, as has been shown, are always present, interacting and interdependent, but the dominant properties of each phase are identifiable. There is a reciprocal relationship with the environment. Genetically, the three phases correspond to the libidinal levels of orality, anality and genitality. The ego begins early in the form of a patchwork of ego boundaries between the divisions of the structural and topological aspects of the personality, and achieves its relative maximum during the voluntary psychophysiological phase. The role of the environment is best observed when viewed from the economic and dynamic points of view. That is to say, the way in which bodily needs are met and bodily tensions are relieved will determine the manifest expression of states of tension or deprivation. Similarly, the modes of deferment of gratification and the development of other pleasure-seeking capacities are strongly influenced by the environment.

By means of constitutional reflex mechanisms, the voluntary component can become associated with a variety of involuntary processes which in themselves have no primary psychic representation. Secondarily, however, the manifestations of such functions can reach consciousness by means of the subjective sensations they arouse. Disturbances of respiratory rate, rhythm and volume affect muscle tone, shivering, heart rate, peripheral vascular tone, skin temperature and subjective cutaneous sensations. Many of these signs and symptoms are the familiar somatic experiences of anxiety. Alterations in tone of the anal sphincter through reflex efforts on peristaltic tone of the colon, and perhaps the small bowel, can induce abdominal distention, flatulence and constipation. The psychological processes which utilize these voluntary motor mechanisms vary considerably. It should be emphasized that innumerable psychic components fuse with relatively few somatic effectors to produce the limited number of psychophysiologic states (moods and affects) of which the human being is capable. Anger, laughing, weeping, depression or elation, anxiety are each the end points of infinitely varied details of mental contents.

With further maturation and experience, the voluntary system, mostly the musculoskeletal apparatus, becomes ascendant. The various sensory modalities become included to the extent that they are volitionally directed by means of the purposive voluntary motor apparatus. Here the psychic representation potentially achieves the closest approximation to reality. At the stage when the voluntary system becomes dominant, the organism's capacity to differentiate stimuli and appropriate responses are relatively advanced in comparison with the earlier involuntary stages. Moreover, the capacity for environmental mastery is considerably developed.

By and large, the effort to control function in the interest of adaptation occurs in the first three years of life. This corresponds to the dominance of the involuntary functional and the narcissistic phase of development. The ego develops progressively but is not yet ascendant. The libidinal stages of orality and anality and the anlagen for further psychic differentiation are established in this period. These events are analogous to the field theories of modern experimental embryology which hold that in relatively undifferentiated states of development, certain tissues contain "organizers" or potentials for differentiation into heterogeneous organs and tissues from an apparently homogeneous state. These "organizers" are always present, but can only exert their influence "normally" when the proper conditions of preceding development and of the environment are present. The instincts, as viewed by psychoanalysts, operate as "organizers" in the psychic sphere and serve to mobilize constitutional and biological and environmental factors into a variety of differentiates of function, behavior and psychic representation. Moreover, as in experimental embryology, the earlier in the process of differentiation an "irregularity" occurs, the larger the number of derivatives that will reflect a disturbance. This is consistent with psychoanalytic theory, in that prognosis and disability tend to vary with the libidinal stage in which the fixation has occurred. The earlier the trauma the larger the number of aspects of the personality that will be affected.

When the musculoskeletal, sphincter and respiratory control and speech become established, a voluntary component comes into force. The timing for the introduction of voluntary control in relation to biological maturation, and the psychic capacity to differentiate stimuli calling for voluntary control, is of paramount importance for the subsequent patterns which the given function will assume. The capacity to differentiate stimuli must be emphasized. In development, many processes and events are proceeding simultaneously. As a result, the stimulus for voluntary control (usually a demand for inhibition of a previously involuntary function) may become associated with more than one function, including irrelevant ones.

When the development begins to include the capacity for object relations, the structures and functions involved are more related to mastery of objects and circumstances in the environment. Libidinally, this corresponds to phallic, urethral and genital stages. Structurally, in this phase, the ego and its functions of perception, integration and execution in the interests of adaptation and defense, receive the most intense implementation up to that time.

In terms of this systematization and in accord with the definition of psychosomatic medicine, every disease has the potential for psychopathology in the psychic representation of the organ functions involved. This potential is determined by genetic, dynamic and structural factors in the organic, psychological and environmental spheres. Clinically, it may be significant etiologically or as a concomitant or as a sequel in the disease. For example, a disease may result when an organ function is brought under inadequately developed ego control. As a result of premature control by an ego limited in its capacity for differentiating stimuli, the function is conditionally related to too large a group of stimuli, or to an inappropriate stimulus. Hence, hyperfunctioning and hypofunctioning of intestines, stomach, lungs, muscle tone and posture as well as regressive forms of function in these organs are some of the maladaptive consequences. This so-called organ fixation may result from pathologically intense stimulation of the function during infancy, such as might be produced by an infection involving the function (Deutsch and Nadell, 3), or from intense environmental stresses and demands which create highly specific conflict situations (Alexander and French, 1).

These events act as genetic determinants and can be dynamically modified as noted above. The organism can regress to these fixation points; i.e., to an infantile stage of undifferentiated physical responses. Primitive, widely fluctuating and generalized forms of function come into play which are maladaptive for the adult. Characteristic of such responses are the lability and wide fluctuations in the intensity and frequency of the function, and varying degrees of inhibition of voluntary control.

The psychophysiological development of the infant can be divided into three stages. Each appears to have distinguishing characteristics in terms of: (a) organ cathexis; (b) differentiation of stimuli in relation to response; (c) degree of central regulation versus organ autonomy; (d) primary and secondary affects; (e) homeostatic boundaries; (f) reciprocal relation of ego development to environment; (g) dominance of functional system; i.e., voluntary or involuntary or both; (h) effect of regression on tissue pathology; (i) psychological character of regression; (j) prognosis and implications for therapy.

The developmental stages are:

1. Initial oral, involuntary, preverbal phase with undifferentiated stimuli provoking mass somatic responses. Moods and affects express only tension and gratification. Regression to this level results in the highest degree of tissue pathology, and highest degree of psychotic substrate. Therapy is primarily anaclitic; i.e., restoration of optimum psychophysiological equilibrium by reënacting idealized mother-infant relationship.

2. Transitional anal, partial voluntary with partial differentiation of stimuli provoking unrelated patterned somatic responses. Moods and affects are partially differentiated, with fragile capacity for object relationships. Therapy is anaclitic with subsequent symbolic interpretation. High degree of tissue pathology. Large psychotic substrate.

3. Genital, voluntary, verbal with high degree of quantitative and qualitative specificity of somatic response to stimuli. High degree of differentiation of mood and affect responses. Therapy almost exclusively on a transference level. Least tissue pathology. Least psychotic substrate.

Different patients with so-called psychosomatic diseases exhibit all degrees of severity of their illnesses. Those that are seen in the hospital are obviously the sickest examples; that is, the pathophysiology is more profound, the tissue pathology more extensive and the response to therapy is less favorable. In this hospitalized group, careful psychiatric and psychological examination not infrequently discloses an underlying psychotic personality substrate. Such patients not uncommonly alternate psychological disturbances with their physical disease. The pregenital features of their character make-up are marked. They tend to show pseudoneurotic defenses against psychosis. The antecedent events of a relapse of their disease are more often insidious and not generally preceded by a so-called catastrophe. Endogenous factors seem to prevail over exogenous ones. It is relatively easy to structure such patients in terms of a complex of defenses according to personality profiles, or according to pregenital dynamisms. After all, these are highly regressed character organizations where such psychological findings are universal regardless of the physical or psychological disease. Freud has frequently stressed the significance of the universality of certain levels in the unconscious.

On the other hand, the same diseases more often than not run a much more benign course and often are associated with a correspondingly more favorable psychological organization. These patients are found in our outpatient clinics and in the private offices of internists. They are rarely sent to psychiatrists since they generally experience a remission while under the therapeutic relationship with a nonpsychiatric physician.

Hence, from a psychosomatic point of view, we have the same disease with different levels of psychophysiological regression. The prognosis and comprehensive therapy are dependent not only on the disease per se but on the developmental level or stage which is dominant in the patient as a whole. This is another consideration which tends to make the profile and specificity concepts difficult to apply, for these would have to be different in different patients with the same disease according to the regression or fixation level manifested.

These concepts have profound implications for therapy. Very sick patients with ulcerative colitis, regional ileitis, asthma or duodenal ulcer appear to do best when the comprehensive management includes what is generally referred to as superficial psychotherapy. More stable varieties of these illnesses achieve the same benefits when treated by internists who are endowed with the intuitive art of medicine. In a recent study of the nature of the patient-physician relationship occurring in such therapeutic successes, it was concluded that iatrogenic regression superimposed on the spontaneous regression in the sick patient favored physiological remission (Margolin, 13). The psychophysiological factor that seemed most regularly correlated with the relapse or remission was a highly specific mood state. The actual content of the psychological interpretations and explanations were not specific except as they affected the patient's mood. Hence, nonverbal communications in the form of attitudes and actions are often most effective, particularly if the patient's regressive wishes are gratified.

Similarly, diseases which affect the voluntary functions and which are generally classified as conversion hysterias, generally have the best prognosis. Yet here too, it is advantageous to apply the principle of correlating the syndrome with the developmental level manifested in the psychological and physiological regression. Hysterical symptoms occur in psychoses and in regressively fixated characters in whom the second phase of tissue damage is often marked.

In short, in each disease we are dealing with permutations and combinations of genetic and dynamic somatic and psychological factors. Diagnosis must be based on this consideration if therapy is to be rational.

These views have the potential merit of rendering psychosomatic that which has been empirically observed psychoanalytically. They may provide methods for the independent verification and for the validation of certain inferences and constructs based on these data. Moreover, and what is operationally important, they treat psychoanalytic psychology as a property of general biological processes and principles. The terminology of psychoanalysis can be harmonized with that of the universal biological mechanisms on which it has always been based. This does not mean that there are no psychological data. On the contrary, it makes it possible to distinguish more clearly what position given psychic processes occupy in the body-mind dialectical continuum.

For clinical purposes, the elaboration up to this point of the thesis of this paper can be applied to the further analysis of other psychosomatic phenomena. To begin again with the biological basis, the research on localization of functions in the brain has shown that at least two forms exist. The first is illustrated by the classical Brodmann map which is an architectural cortical representation of parts of the body. It is phylogenetically determined and is a fixed species characteristic of homo sapiens. Within limited variations, given specific responses can be predicted by neurophysiological exploration. The second form of localization as exemplified by Papez's theory of emotion consists of syncytial networks of acquired experiences, of learned motor skills and associated affects. To illustrate this, the hand has a specific motor localization in the precentral gyrus and a sensory representation in the postcentral area. Penfield has shown that the functions of the hand in terms of experience fused with psychological significance are localized in different ways in the temporal-parietal lobes. The modes by which this conditionally determined anatomy is expressed in the form of somatic symptoms has not been demonstrated. At best, fragments exist which can only be brought together by way of a speculative synthesis, such as formulated by Kubie (9). Clinically, however, one can distinguish between so-called organic and functional affections of the hand. The former correspond to the pattern of neuroanatomic constitutionally determined localization. The latter disturbance demonstrates the disturbance of acquired function in relation to affectively charged experiences. To put it another way, we "know" our hand not in terms of its neural and structural anatomy and phylogenesis, but in terms of the sensations, functions and experiences associated with it.

To the extent that one's conception of the operation of the body and its parts are derived by sensations and subjective experience, one can speak of a "fantasy of function,"[3] or perhaps an "illusion of function." Schilder's (17) concept of the "body image" is a relevant aspect. In general, these fantasies of function undergo continuous modification under the abrasive influence of

[3] Waller, Kaufman and Deutsch (19) used the concept of "fantasy of function" to designate a specific type of fantasy that was elaborated and acted out in the somatic sphere of patients with anorexia nervosa. This usage should be distinguished from that developed in this paper. Here the concept is used as a general principle underlying psychophysiological development.

reality testing. The alteration of these fantasies in the direction of reality may occur as part of a learning process in the conflictless sphere of the ego, or may be rendered conflictfree by means of sublimation in vocation, art or scientific activity. Repression on a conflictual basis can result in certain consequences, for the fantasy of function is different at various stages of development and at various ages. It is especially marked at the psychophysiological transition points such as weaning, bowel training, speech and motility training, puberty and overt sexuality. This succession of fantasies of function becomes part of the unconscious. They emerge in dreams, free associations, in our daydreams and in neurotic and psychotic symptoms.

The psychic representation of an organ and its function is a complex in which the anatomic cortical localization is constitutionally determined and beyond certain limits relatively invariable. The psychic representation can and does undergo enormous modifications, according to the genetic development and experiences of the individual. His awareness and fantasy of the structure and function of an organ is different, for example, at one, two, five, thirteen and fifty years of age. In part, this results from actual organic alteration in form and function, changes in the capacity to perceive and integrate these events, and finally experiences which affect both the alterations and their perception. Other elements in the complex are related to environmental compliance and resistance, and the special determining experiences associated with the expression of the function of the organ. In other words, the development of the psychic representation proceeds *pari passu* with the evolution of the personality and its perceptual, integrative, executive and adaptive mechanisms.

The psyche, however, has no awareness of anatomical and physiological localization except in so far as it is learned intellectually, as for example, by a physician. Such knowledge, however, differs from that which involves sensory perceptions resulting from the functions of an organ. This kind of information, incidentally, is of no prophylactic value whatsoever. Cardiologists with so-called cardiac neuroses have been seen and treated. Only those functions and organs which can be experienced directly or indirectly are recorded. These perceptions combine associatively with other sensations and experiences and are elaborated into a conception or fantasy of the structure and function of the organ which may or may not bear any relationship to the reality perceived by the physiologist, pathologist or psychologist.

The psychoanalysis of a diabetic adolescent boy whose disease was difficult to control, illustrates some of these features of the "fantasy of function" concept.

Up to the age of sixteen, it never occurred to him that he was in any conflict with his parents—mother in particular. At that time, he developed diabetes, and subsequently sought psychotherapy because of characterological difficulties which followed. With diabetes, a struggle with his parents began which was characterized by nonconformist behavior. He was deliberately rebellious and defiant.

He had the fantasy that his mother withdrew love from him and that such love was symbolized by food. His diabetes, in a sense, was a disorder of utilizing food and, in his case, was marked by excessive hunger and thirst; i.e., a persistent demand for that which mother allegedly withdrew from him. He equated sweets with mother's milk. The autonomous activity of his viscera was repeatedly equated with his mother doing things for him—i.e., she too functioned autonomously in an effort to keep him in physiological equilibrium.

The diabetes compelled him voluntarily to provide a function which had previously been involuntary. Thus he had to reject his mother and "run his own pancreas." Because of this conflict he had intermittent difficulty in managing his diabetes, and his conflict with his mother had increased.

He also regarded his diabetes both as a claim upon his mother's love and as an expression of his drive to be independent of her. With regard to the latter, he conceived of the inside of his body and of his mother as both serving the same function of keeping him free of tension and in constant equilibrium. Hence, his tendency to keep himself in acidosis and in ketonuria meant that he was living on his own fat; i.e, living on his own insides. In this way he was self-sufficient and yet symbolically reëxperiencing his mother's automatic and sustained attention. Similarly, his regulation of his own insulin intake represented his independence of his own insides. He is weaned from the autonomic functions of his own body.

To return to the exposition of the concept of psychophysiological regression,[4] there is a gradient with age, in the width of certain homeostatic boundaries. These

[4] Dr. Joseph M. Michaels (16) and Dr. Ives Hendrick (6) have each independently called attention to the concept which in this paper is referred to as "physiological regression."

are widest in infancy and become progressively narrower with age. The tissue tolerance for these fluctuations decreases similarly. Hence, a physiological regression, like a psychological regression, is inappropriate at the time it appears, in that the variations in function exceed the tolerance of the tissues or the psyche. In other words, a function which at one time (in infancy) was appropriate, tolerable and compensable, can become inappropriate, non-tolerable and decompensating in later years.

The concept of regression is used both in the psychoanalytic and biologic sense. Biologically, regression in the structure of a tissue results in the appearance of cell forms and of functional properties which had existed previously in the process of differentiation. In other words, regression includes dedifferentiation or a reversal of the vectors of differentiation. Physiologically, the functions react more to peripheral stimuli and are more dissociated from central regulatory control, under which the function had become a part of the total economy of the organism.

Illustrative of such psychophysiologically regressed manifestations is the case of an elderly man with fecal incontinence. Detailed physical examination failed to disclose a cause for this symptom except for a markedly relaxed anal sphincter. Psychologically, however, the incontinence occurred in a setting in which his waning powers had interfered with his ability to support himself financially and socially. When he was given a cathartic, however, he exhibited adequate sphincter control. His incontinence expressed both his helplessness and his rebellion. The defecation due to the purgative was not in the service of this regression. The medication was administered by physicians (parent surrogates to whom he once conformed). Although he was incapable of psychological insight, therapy was possible by exploiting regressive transference capacities.

Another patient, a thirteen-year-old girl with complete hysterical motor paralysis of her lower extremities, began to recover with psychotherapy. One leg recovered before the other. During this time, she walked with a broad based gait, circumducting the affected leg. There was also an inhibition of the normal associated movements of the upper extremity on that side. Physiologically, she manifested the motility of a child before its third year. Analogous changes have been induced by means of hypnotic regression.

The regression invariably involves the giving up or inhibition of the appropriate mastery of physiological and psychological responses. This phenomenon is not necessarily pathological. It may be in the service of recovery from a noxious process. An infection will produce embryonal reactions in the tissues, marked lability in the regulation of bodily equilibria and a form of psychic dependency, helplessness and passivity characterized by a narcissistic relation to people and objects in the environment. This form of regressive reaction enhances the bodily defensive mechanisms on the one hand and provokes the environmental attention and protection on the other.

A sick person is always a child, so to speak, in his relation to the physician. But just as children vary in their behavior, so will the manifestations of the regressive behavior vary. The regression becomes critically pathological when the psychic state becomes inaccessible to object relations and influence, and when the physical function becomes detached from central organized control and reacts autonomously.

Regression rarely brings about an exact replica of an infantile state of affairs. It almost invariably carries back with it some of the acquired learning and experiences from the years through which it has retreated. Moreover, the total organism does not regress, only parts of it, and then only in varying degrees. As a result, the picture of a sick individual, in terms of the regression hypothesis, is a mosaic consisting of elements in varying states of regression and maturity.

In conclusion, I should like to make a brief synthesis of the several streams of facts, hypotheses and speculations that have been presented. In essence, it has been submitted that psychosomatic symptoms are regressive psychophysiological states. Repressed fantasies of function return as psychophysiological components of mood and affect states. The more archaic the fantasy of function, the more autonomously the organ functions, and the less central integrative regulation participates. The brain, so to speak, disregards the organ which ceases to operate in the interests of a coördinated economy. The organ acts as though infantile homeostatic boundaries were present. The tissues, however, have lost their tolerance for the infantile fluctuations. Hence, a decompensating situation develops and disability is the result. The choice of organ is determined by the way in which the primary affect or mood component of the infantile psychophysiological state is displaced, condensed or dissociated. If the primary affect is genetically associated with oral weaning, defenses are developed against the overdetermined significance of separation. Every new demand on the developing ego and body economy becomes a potentially pathological stimulus. Similarly, if this process occurs in later stages of development, when a greater capacity for differentiating stimuli is present, the pathophysiologic responses are progressively more localized and specific.

Thus, each psychosomatic manifestation can have several levels of organic and psychological regression, with significant differences in prognosis and therapy. The role of moods and affects and the lack of specificity of content is greatest in the most regressed fantasies of function and least in the most differentiated fantasies of function. Hence superficial psychotherapy (in the special sense described above) is more effective for the former and insight therapy is possible for the latter.

Regardless of the ultimate form assumed by the solutions to these problems, these conceptions have been of operational value. They have indicated areas of research and the principles of practice and theory that I have used. Hence we are investigating anaclitic therapy in relation to iatrogenic regression, the psychophysiological aspects of moods and affects, and of pathophysiological manifestations such as uterine dystocia and cardiac arrhythmias. In other words, it is hoped that research and the accumulation of data will modify these hypotheses in continuously fruitful directions.

BIBLIOGRAPHY

1. ALEXANDER, F. and FRENCH, T. M.: *Studies in Psychosomatic Medicine*. Ronald Press, New York, 1948.
2. DEUTSCH, F.: The Use of the Psychosomatic Concept in Medicine. *Bull. Johns Hopkins Hosp.*, 80:71-85, 1947.
3. DEUTSCH, F. and NADELL, R.: Psychosomatic Aspects of Dermatology with Special Consideration of Allergic Phenomena. *Nerv. Child*, 5:339-364, 1946.
4. DUNBAR, F.: *Emotions and Bodily Changes*. Columbia University Press, New York, 1938.
5. FEDERN, P.: Ichgrenzen, Ichstärke und Identifizierung. *Almanach der Psychoanalyse*, 1937.
6. HENDRICK, I.: Cited by L. W. Sontag, pp. 55-56 in *Synopsis of Psychosomatic Diagnosis*, ed. F. Dunbar. C. V. Mosby, St. Louis, 1948.
7. JANOWITZ, H. D. and GROSSMAN, M. I.: Hunger and Appetite. Some Definitions and Concepts. *J. Mt. Sinai Hosp.*, 16:231-240, 1949.
8. KUBIE, L. S.: A Theoretical Application to Some Neurological Problems of the Proportions of Excitation Waves Which Move in Closed Circuits. *Brain*, 53:166-177, 1930.
9. KUBIE, L. S.: Some Implications for Psychoanalysis of Modern Concepts of Organization of the Brain. Abstracted in *Bull. Am. Psa. Assoc.*, 8:198-199, 1952.
10. MCCLEOD, A., WITTKOWER, E., and MARGOLIN, S. G.: Basic Concepts in Psychosomatic Medicine. In *Recent Developments in Psychosomatic Medicine*. London, 1953 (in press).
11. MARGOLIN, S. G.: The Meaning of Psychogenesis in Organ Symptoms. Presented at the Connecticut Seminars on Psychiatry and Neurology. Hartford, Conn., March 2, 1951 (in press).
12. MARGOLIN, S. G.: Cited by Robert Cleghorn in *Recent Developments in Psychosomatic Medicine*. London, 1953 (in press).
13. MARGOLIN, S. G.: Psychophysiological Studies of Fistulous Openings into the Gastrointestinal Tract. *J. Mt. Sinai Hosp.* 1953 (in press).
14. MARGOLIN, S. G. and KAUFMAN, M. R.: What Is Psychosomatic Medicine? *Med. Clin. North America, New York Number*: 609-610, 1948.
15. MCCULLOCH, W. S.: Functional Organization of the Cerebral Cortex. *Physiol. Rev.*, 24:390-407, 1944.
16. MICHAELS, J. J.: A Psychiatric Adventure in Comparative Pathophysiology of the Infant and Adult. *J. Nerv. & Ment. Dis.*, 100: 49-63, 1944.

17. SCHILDER, P.: *The Image and Appearance of the Human Body.* International Universities Press, New York, 1950.
18. SPITZ, R. A.: Hospitalism. An Inquiry into the Genesis of Psychiatric Conditions in Early Childhood. *The Psychoanalytic Study of the Child, 1*:53-73. International Universities Press, New York, 1945.
19. WALLER, J. V., KAUFMAN, M. R., and DEUTSCH, F.: Anorexia Nervosa, A Psychosomatic Entity. *Psychosom. Med., 2*:3-16, 1940.

SOME CURRENT TRENDS AND HYPOTHESES OF PSYCHOSOMATIC RESEARCH

ROY R. GRINKER, M.D.[1]

I

Analysis of the latest formulations of each important investigative group in psychosomatic medicine indicates that there has been a trend toward agreement and a tolerant acceptance of pluralistic concepts of etiology and mechanism. Our public and scientific pronouncements indicate confidence in our premises and trust in our methods. It seems, however, that this consensus is by no means justified. In the first place, rarely has the psychosomatic field been approached from the point of view that it is a field. Correlations have been made between selected somatic dysfunctions and supposedly connected, related, or causal specific feelings (1). Genetic or current concomitants of such psychological and physical disturbances are adopted as criteria of psychosomatic unity.

Although a field is a continuum as far as its time and space dimensions are concerned, it is not homogeneous but contains identifiable foci or nodes of organization,

[1] From the Institute for Psychosomatic and Psychiatric Research and Training of the Michael Reese Hospital, Chicago.

among which are included the soma and the psyche. Each node may be categorized by three determinants; one, the constitutional determinants which include the content, substance, or basic components of each system; two, the integrative determinants which include those processes which sustain the structure in function or maintain order within the focus of organization; and three, the system determinants that characterize the function of the system as a part of the field and which can only be determined by observing the transactions of the system among other systems (16).

The total field does not comprise only somatic and psychic foci but also group, society, and culture as transacting systems within a universe in a four-dimensional continuum. All parts of the field are in reciprocal relationship with each other. Our current psychosomatic formulations are apparently structuralized within too small a frame of space and too narrow a segment of time to fit into a field theory. In fact, most observers do not clearly indicate their position, and if they do, conclusions are stated as though they were observing the entire field. Often the systems of psyche and soma are reported as though they had developed and continued to function in a vacuum devoid of other human individuals, groups, or culture. Let us attempt to analyze where some of the observers of the field are actually placed according to their reports.

Some observers view a specific organ's changing function against the background of spontaneously or experimentally induced life situations, correlated with the concomitant emotional reactions experienced consciously and reported by the subject or from interpretations of his behavior (*17*). The functional alterations observed are stereotyped, and variability exists only in the shifting site of the organic changes, although no observer has viewed any significant combination of organs to determine simultaneity or succession of activity, or a shifting interaction of innervation. Other investigators view some unconscious emotional processes, without going to the depth of the most significant experiences occurring at a preverbal age, against the background of remissions and recrudescences of a specific disturbance under scrutiny. These disturbances are located at a site corresponding to the presenting complaint or dysfunction, and are often measured inadequately and too infrequently (*1*). Another group views the behavior patterns of individuals against the background of a general organ-system disturbance as though it were a steady state. In such a procedure, the organ dysfunction is accepted as a stereotype from the diagnosis, and the behavior patterns are reconstructed from the history of the patient and his relatives without the benefit of direct observation (*6*). Still other observers who are more interested in the social aspects of the field view the individual as a statistic, not identifiable as a person, against the background of a generalized, unmeasurable, social state (*12*).

All these workers promulgate conclusions regarding the genesis, the meaning, and the effects of psychosomatic-social processes, although observations are made from different and not identifiable frames of reference. In spite of lip service to multiple causality the approach of each group permits only a circumscribed view of the field which is much larger in time and space than each identifies. The absence of any one investigator's capacity to describe and measure more than a single aspect of the field, and for that matter to take a position at more than one point at a time, makes it necessary for him to work with other investigators. One observer describing a small sector of the field from an identifiable position can delineate the boundaries at which his operational methods cease to function, and relegate to another observer with other techniques the task of describing and measuring the changes in his system. Once an initial field approach to any situation is utilized and the system foci under observation are defined, all others should be identified as constant variables. However, since the psychosomatic-social field exists simultaneously in time, the most effective means of dealing with several systems in transaction is the utilization of multiple observers at different frames of reference measuring changes in activities *at the same time* (as close as possible).

The time element brings into consideration the difficulties in making valid statements concerning the development of somatic functions as foci from an unintegrated system. Psychiatric investigations into psychosomatic problems usually utilize the technique of psychoanalysis. From data obtained by such reconstructions most current basic assumptions are derived. How deep these analyses go, that is, how far they penetrate into past time and what somatic signals they use, are of utmost significance, yet these variables are rarely accounted for. The utilization of several cross-sections of transactional activity among somatic, psychic and environmental systems at various times could give us a better idea of the longitudinal processes.

II

At birth the infantile organism seems to exist in its greatest state of unification, undifferentiation or wholeness. At that time the imprint and meaning of stimuli are difficult to detect, but the global nature of the infant's activities and reactions can be observed. In response to an internal need such as hunger or thirst, or in reaction to an external stimulus such as cold, the child's total available motor and secretory functions seem to be activated. Within a few months as it comes to recognize the meaningful and significant people in its environment, separation or desertion serve as similar external stimuli in the psychological field. No matter whether internal or external, somatic or psychological, the child has a similar pattern of total behavior in response to frustration of its needs. It cries, salivates, regurgitates, and defecates; its face becomes red, and vigorous random movements occur in muscles of the trunk and appendages. It functions with everything it has available, responding with a total pattern in mass action, synchronously and in integration.

We do not know the meaning that various stimuli may have upon the child except in so far as we are able to project ourselves or anthropomorphize the child's preverbal feelings. However, we can identify the various reactions as indicating responses to stress or deprivation and significant as precursors to fear and anger. To whatever the nature of the stress, the reaction is stereotyped

41

and all organ systems seem to participate with reactions of ejection, riddance, evasion or avoidance. There is little discrimination of response or part response to a stress situation.

The adult under certain circumstances may experience a revival of these general reactions. The war and other traumatic neuroses developing under severe stress are clinical examples of revival of total patterns of activity during the acute or emergency phases (11). At this time peripheral circulatory changes, crying, vomiting, diarrhea, random incoördinated muscular movements, infantile postures, stuttering, etc., are clearly revivals of mass responses of undifferentiated activities.

Most investigators of the psychosomatic field are impressed by the stereotypical nature of the basic emotional constellations that are expressed only in the symptom. In many psychosomatic disturbances of adults, characterized by fluctuations related to states of emotional tension, there appear monotonously the triad of dependency, frustration and hostility at an early level of oral needs (4). Similarities of psychodynamic trends are more characteristic than differences. The expression of such emotional constellations in thought, fantasy, action or psychological syndromes is prevented, although *pari passu* with their repression certain specific types of characterological defenses appropriate to what is defended against may develop.

Through the vagaries of life situations, or the accidents of special relationships, or the use of pharmacological or other therapies such as cortisone etc., defenses may crumble and the psychosomatic syndrome is superseded by a psychotic breakdown. In such a breakdown

42

the exposed psychodynamics and the type of psychosis is not specific to any special type of psychosomatic disorder previously observed.

A particular psychosomatic expression is not constantly related to a specific emotional constellation. Psychotherapy or psychoanalysis may shift the symptom from one system to another. It is a well-known observation that symptoms may vary spontaneously (crying-migraine, asthma-eczema). It has been shown experimentally that in individuals free from skin diseases, increased transudation occurs through the skin when weeping is inhibited and the appropriate stimulus for weeping is suggested under hypnosis (14). Furthermore, when eczematous patients are given the suggestion to weep lachrymally, their normally weeping skin is less permcable for transudation.

\ In almost all psychosomatic disturbances induced by life situations the disordered physiology is in the nature of hypersecretion, hyperemia and hypermotility (17). The hypersecretion or increase in free fluid seems to be a primary and fundamental physiological reaction accompanying an otherwise psychological set of primary dependency. As the ego boundaries diminish in a severely regressive state the permeability of cellular membranes increases, a correlation which should stimulate much speculation regarding primitive ways of maintaining homeostatic balance as contrasted with more developed and evolved enzymatic and neural methods.

Such observations as I have selectively cited seem to indicate that primary vegetative reactions to stress or need are undifferentiated; that severe regressive modes of response to catastrophic stress in adult life repeat the early infantile pattern; and that, when discrete fragments of this general response are present, they are interchangeable under certain circumstances. Furthermore, both the basic psychodynamics and physiological dynamics of fragmentary visceral dysfunctions are more alike than dissimilar. These observations naturally stimulate our interest in the origin of the fragments of the total pattern and how the parts are linked to the whole.

III

The human infantile organism becoming detached from its mother is born with certain built-in hereditary functional patterns which are innate to its structures and are part of its phylogenetic inheritance. Some differences or variations may be genotypic and constitutional, others have occurred in the numerous processes of intrauterine development. Many differences arise from prenatal influences dependent upon the mother's physical and emotional health and behavior, or as a result of the duration and vicissitudes of passage through the birth canal.

At first the organism *acts* on its environment through its wound-up patterns of functions, since its sensory and perceptive systems are not well developed. They come into action later and only then permit the organism to respond in reaction to its environment. As an undifferentiated whole committed only to those structuralized functions that are species bound, the infant has his highest degree of potentiality, but also the highest degree of sensitivity, because stimuli impinging on him early affect all of him, no matter how much differentia-

44

tion later occurs. The homologue in biology is the effect of trauma on multipotential embryonic tissue whose resulting differentiating parts carry an imprint in their subsequent organization. Later traumatic events acting on a more organized structure or function are limited in site and localization of effect.

The infant's first responses show very little variation in type from individual to individual. They occur when a threshold level is reached which may be high or low, depending upon the general reservoir of available energy, the degree of sensitivity and the extent of responsiveness. At birth, infants may be grossly categorized as to their rapidity of reaction to the environment and the quantity of motor or secretory activity within such responses.

The responsiveness of the infant at birth is unconditioned and generalized within the limits of his species' capacity to action. Coghill (13) clearly proved that in amblystoma total swimming movements first appear and that when stimulated the organism always responds with the same type of general movements out of which differentiation develops. Such differentiation is in the nature of individual reflex activity through functions of part of those structures which were originally involved in the total movement patterns. The individuation or differentiation of movements utilize part of what was present at birth in mass action. In all species the type and extent of differentiation is limited by their available organization, but learning also influences both dimensions of such differentiation within the organizational possibilities.

Although arising from and utilizing parts of total

45

action processes, the total pattern is never lost because under certain circumstances it may again assume dominance. The asynchronous activities of individual processes may be again superseded by a synchronous coördinated total pattern. In fact, Coghill has stated that the part derived from the whole persists in functional conflict with the whole for dominance. Margolin (15) demonstrated that the activities of the exposed resting adult human stomach are out-of-phase and become in-phase in response to feeding or stress. This does not mean anarchy in that each part-function struggles to maintain its supremacy over other parts and against the whole. An orderly integration develops among the differentiated patterns with determinant functions which defend against disintegration. The embryogenesis of differentiation of part patterns and their integration to form a new whole is an important subject which concerns not only embryologists but also physiologists and psychologists.

Probably nowhere is this process of differentiation and reintegration more clearly expressed in a psychological sense than in some of Freud's (8) early formulations of zones of libidinal organization. He postulated several levels of expression of psychic energy which depend upon the development and readiness of a hierarchy of organs, all of them eventually relinquishing their roles to become part of a new whole; the mature, integrated and genital adult. Should development not proceed normally, under certain conditions disintegration of the whole is associated with regression to more infantile or primitive levels or still further to the less differentiated psychotic state. Out of the total pattern independent part activities develop with spontaneity, autonomy and initiative, and varying rise and fall of dominance, always utilizing part of the total pattern and always capable of relinquishing autonomy to fall back into the old synchronous mass action.

IV

Let us assume that the human organism at birth comprises one undifferentiated functional system not pushed from behind into action nor pulled from outside into reaction, but that it is in transaction with its environment. Out of this global transactional system are precipitated many smaller systems which still remain under the potential dominance of the whole but which are linked with each other in a circular process of transaction just as the total organism is related to its environment. Each system serves as the environment of the other. The intrapersonal functions may be classified into many discrete systems depending upon one's taste for size, but the living boundaries between each are ill-defined, incomplete and variable and dependent upon the transactions occurring at any particular time and place. In fact, one might state that such boundaries correspond to living semipermeable membranes of a single cell. The integration with each system and the defenses against disintegration constitute the forces that tend to maintain a steady state. Health and sickness are only variations in degree of the same processes.

Activity in one system is communicated to all others and stimulates within each of them processes which often are of such small quantity and such short duration that they are not measurable by our existing methods. If a stimulus which impinges on an appropriate system is of such quantity or duration that it constitutes stress, responses will be set into action which tend to return that system to a relatively steady state, but other systems will also be involved in this process. It may be assumed that there is no threshold barrier between systems because of the continuous transaction. When a given system is strained in handling a particular stress, the minor, perhaps unmeasurable preparatory changes in another system become intensified and apparent as another response to the initial stimulus. The integration among the systems is inherent in the first preparatory activity and the later more intense change in response to stress impinging on any one of them. The integration within a single system is dependent upon its capacity to act alone without strain before a new order of action is set off within other systems with which it is in transaction.

In either case, from a single system which may functionally disintegrate because of strain, to all systems and eventually to a total response, activity progressively increases to facilitate the organism's striving to maintain steady internal state. The result is a multiplicity of circular and corrective processes between systems which are oriented toward stabilizing the organism and maintaining its integration. A breakdown between boundaries and an intensification of activity of another system only occurs when the stress becomes too severe. Likewise the total pattern of behavior resumes its primitive infantile total functions when the several systems which have been fractionated out of the total are no longer able to handle the stress. From the initial affect of anxiety or stress in *facilitating* defenses, greater quantities are *destructive* by producing strain and ultimately disintegration, when the differentiated systems are under greatest strain and the whole takes over and the old primitive patterns return.

My attempt has been to demonstrate that whether the organism functions as a primitive whole before differentiation, or is the process of straining in an effort to handle stress, or has been disintegrated by excessive stress into a de-differentiated whole, somatic and psychic systems are in a constant state of transaction with each other. Continuous concomitance of somatic and psychological action patterns may exist apart from the disintegrative effects of stress only as the result of lasting traumatic impressions made upon a total system before differentiation. It is this phenomenon which we are now prepared to examine.

V

Our first question concerns the acquisition of data concerning the early developmental period of infancy and childhood to determine the nature of stimuli or experiences and their result on psyche and soma. The reconstructed data obtained from *psychoanalysis of adults* hardly ever reaches back to what may be termed a crucial period and is interpreted only from the current transference neurosis. Thus it is a faint shadow on the present of what was once a bright light in the past. This is especially true for data published by those analysts willing to accept character defenses as significant primary effects of infantile trauma. *Analysis of children* is a sort of middle ground between reconstruction and direct observation. It reveals much but not enough of current child-mother relationships, and it uncovers early traumata even less clearly than data obtained from adults. *Child observations* have been exploited in the last several decades in a systematic manner, which Gesell and Armatruda (9) call a psychomorphological approach. This work concerns unfolding of a patterned or ontogenetic behavior which is built-in as a species inheritance and involves time sequences of growth relations. This presumes that the embryogenesis of mind is to be found in the development of postural behavior and to a great extent neglects the transactions between child and mother.

Since the work of Freud which called attention to the various zones which differentiate and play a part in libidinal satisfactions of the growing child, attention has been directed toward their unfolding into what may be called psychological modes of dealing with interpersonal relationships. For example, Erikson has drawn elaborate diagrams showing how these zones become modal forces in interpersonal relationships and calls attention to the fact that mutual regulation between the child and the mother, as these zones are developing, determines to a large extent the modes of dealing with life situations (7). The child's desire and the mother's giving, the child's rage and frustration and the mother's punitive attitude, form the psychological gestalts of dealing with and mastering the environment.

Greenacre points out in a general conceptual scheme that the earlier in life that traumatic events occur, the greater effect on the emotional sphere and the more those memories are somatized (10). Severe or prolonged trauma produce a greater effect, using all available channels for the expression of the resultant excitement. In fact, premature activation of libidinal zones results in the utilization of all channels of discharge including those not ready. She emphasizes that the nature, extent and timing of trauma influence the modal organization of the final character structure as viewed in the manner of handling the oedipus complex and other interpersonal problems. Here the Freudian concept of critical vulnerability is highlighted in terms of actual trauma of early childhood.

It has been pointed out that forced feeding, early enemas, excessive cleanliness and excessive or early training of gymnastic skills have a profound effect on the developing neuromuscular mechanism which may later break down. Many children are robbed of infancy or the chance for spontaneous differentiation by stimulation of precocity. The changing patterns of child care seem not only to place a burden on the mother, but also prevent the demarcation of zonal differentiation.

VI

In my opinion the central core of the psychosomatic problem is the period of differentiation from total hereditary to individual learned patterns and their integration into a new personal system. Any hypothesis concerned with psychosomatic functions or disturbances should deal with the intermediate process of development between the undifferentiated whole functional pattern

51

and the integrated matured process. It is this period that determines the formation of healthy, sick or potentially sick organisms.

Previous investigations have dealt with the unfolding of spontaneously developing differentiated patterns as though they occurred in a vacuum, or they have been limited to investigations by which the human environment has handled certain few of the child's budding potentialities. For the most part these have included motoric functions and intaking and eliminative processes (5). Completely mysterious, unobserved and unmeasured are the processes happening in the vast area of the "in-between" carried on by many organs and organ systems innervated by the vegetative nervous system.

There has been little emphasis on the timing of development nor on the reciprocal relationship among the individual portions of the visceral nervous system. Concomitance, coördination, reciprocal inhibition and temporal succession develop from the matrix of diffuse undifferentiated vegetative responses. Many smaller systems become specifically linked to each other through circular self-corrective processes as a result of natural maturation plus special environmental influences which affect not only physiological processes but also the psychological patterns developing at the same time. The hypothesis may be stated that visceral activity is subject to a learning or experiential process which, if impinged upon the undifferentiated organism, influences the process of differentiation and all systems subsequently differentiated, including the psychological.

What aside from heredity is concerned in the development of individual differences must be assumed to be derivatives from the early experiences which impinge upon the child. Variations of patterns within the infant at birth are numerous, but even these are due to more than hereditary destiny. Already cultural attitudes have influenced the child during gestation through degrees of activity of the mother, her diet, the type of clothes she wears, etc. During birth such factors as anesthesia, use of forceps, speed of resuscitation, are influences which act upon the child. Then almost at once the degree of isolation from the mother, the sterility of the nursery, the absence of early postnatal feeding, circumcision, etc., are among variables of early environmental influences which bear on the child.

Sometimes these influences are accidental through serious or prolonged dysfunction as a result of microbic invasion or early enzymatic deficiency. Illness of the infant not only affects it directly but has an effect upon the mother which reverberates back to the child. Often this reaches a point at which parasitic dependency for some function is charactered by the term, "secondary gain." Therese Benedek indicates how the child incorporates the emotional attitudes and anxieties of the mother. She states, "the psychodynamics of symbiosis is interrupted at birth but remains a functioning force directing and motivating mental and somatic interaction between mother and child."

More significant and universal is the effect which mother and her surrogates have on specific conditioned responses. These reflect personal emotional attitudes as developed in her by her own specific past development, the special values of the ethnic group from which she stems, or the general prevailing cultural milieu in which mother and child exist. These attitudes influence the unfolding differentiation within the psychosomatic matrix and are ultimately bound to values. Some functions have high or positive values and are sought or encouraged, some have negative values and are discouraged or prohibited, others are permitted or tolerated in a neutral manner. Furthermore, timing is of great significance in the application of such values.

If the visceral mass responses are permitted and accepted as healthy and expected reactions until the child begins to indicate readiness for differentiation and control, differentiation will occur without loss. Development may occur without deficit and each fraction may persist as silent, utilitarian and adequate responses. On the other hand, when fragments of the total adaptive pattern are prohibited too early before they can be conditioned into appropriate responses, lacunae will appear in the subsequent integration. Rushing the infant in his development through the demand for control, anxious suppression of adaptive responses to intercurrent illness by attitude or medication may obliterate important psychosomatic functions. As a result, adaptive development responses to stress or expressions of anxiety may be diverted to other segments of the visceral pattern. Not only will there be a relative absence of some functions or communications, but an overloading on others. When it is their turn to undergo modification or control by conditioning, more intense or prolonged training becomes necessary.

Anxiety in an adult activates certain visceral patterns which are specific to the individual no matter what the stress, in that each one has his particular way of feeling anxious. Some variations include sinking abdominal sensations, diarrhea, vomiting, dyspnea, sensations of lump in the throat, etc. Out of the generalized infantile precursors of expressions of anxiety each person seems to have been conditioned to certain fragmentary visceral patterns which for him become accurate and faithful harbingers of intrapsychic danger. If the signal intensifies, more previously silent fragments appear until the old generalized infantile pattern is revived in its entirety under conditions of panic or catastrophe. Thus, here too a selective differentiation has occurred in development by some form of conditioning. Under severe stress the conditioned reflexes disappear and diffuse irradiation of excitation reappears. Many other examples of visceral functions modified by external factors acting at various times, may be given. From the day of intrauterine viability to an indefinite end point, a multiplicity of environmental and culturally derived orientations act on the infant. These variables with their infinite permutations cannot help us to create specific psychosomatic patterns until we know enough to classify them into categories according to some significant parameter.

What are the operational procedures by which mother figures may influence the differentiating visceral patterns, aside from interfering with intaking and eliminative functions, or by intensifying motor control in degree or by its premature application? If we were satisfied with these influences we would be content with the zonal and vector hypotheses of Freud and Alexander respectively, but neither of these adequately account for the internal or "in-between" processes. This is truly a vast area of neglected research for which I believe, however, observations, experimentation and measurements are possible.

VII

Let us turn now to a discussion of the psychological derivatives of the primal psychosomatic organization and postulate what variations of function may be expected from early impressions at periods of differentiation. Early ego instincts are originally fused with what are to become libidinal instincts, both functioning in the service of physiology. Both ego and libidinal instincts at first have the same object—mother, nourishment and self. As differentiation occurs they become opposing forces and enter into conflict. Individual differences plus maternal attitudes mold memory traces and determine the subsequent type and degree of such conflicts (3).

It is our present conception that the psychological manifestations of visceral functions form shifting body images which vary with age and conditioning and that their central representations are of functions rather than structure. The cortical homonculus probably varies with functional patterns. First functions of the vegetative nervous system are in the service of anabolism and catabolism. However, because of infections, stresses or excessive demands, the number of stimuli may exceed what the child is able to cope with even in its large homeostatic range. Later in life such range is progressively decreased, and it is less possible for the individual to deal with the variety of stresses arising from organ systems. This restriction can be observed also in the increasing amount of fast and low voltage cortical potentials with less capacity for the return to larger and slower waves under forced ventilation or drowsy states in the electroencephalogram, and the increasing rigid adherence to detail and specificity with lack of global perspective in psychological tests of older persons.

When some early visceral patterns are negatively conditioned and, therefore, the full development of differentiated stress reactors and ego span is restricted, a greater load is placed on what is permitted to function. In addition, the differentiated ego is burdened with the task of devoting a large share of its energy in defense against inhibited visceral responses and their psychological homologue to insure their nonrecurrence, and becomes impoverished and less free. The resultant effects differ little from the defensive armoring, reaction formations, countercathexis with which we are so familiar. It is these defensives that give us the most reliable clues as to what silent activity has been rigorously inhibited by early conditioning. Also the permitted fragments of activity have become more activated as substitute outlets for energy and require greater quantities of countercathexis from the ego. The restricted ego span becomes associated with a lack of plasticity, a greater rigidity, as well as a greater susceptibility to disintegration.

The loaded and weighted portion of the autonomic nervous system and its psychological homologue is often precariously inhibited because there is not enough available energy. Therefore, when ill-advised therapeutic maneuvers liberate these fragments of repressed activity, the ego succumbs and disintegrates. As Therese Benedek states, "the ego remains at a primitive level of conditioning and when beset by too much anxiety for too long, eventually breaks down" (2).

VIII

In order to summarize the hypotheses discussed above I shall list them now in order of chronological primacy.

1. The infant is born with a significantly variable hereditary or built-in visceral behavior pattern which can be measured as a base line on which subsequent influences impinge and produce alterations.

2. The neonatal organism with whatever differentiations apparent at birth functions viscerally as a whole with generalized patterns of reaction to all stress, internal or external.

3. Subsequent maturation is associated with differentiation into part functions with shifting gradients of dominance and part-whole relations, with latency, but not extinction, of dominance of the neonatal whole pattern of functioning.

4. Such differentiation of part functions develops a new and highly individual integration of intrapersonal transacting systems.

5. These systems are foci of a field in a time-space continuum and are characterized by constitutional, integrative and functional determinants. They are in transactional relationship with each other.

6. The neonatal whole pattern as well as the subsequently differentiated functions, even though served by neuronal nets of the vegetative nervous system, are

capable of development and modification by conditioning before the advent of exteroceptive functions or object awareness.

7. This learning develops from stimuli emanating from the external (mother) or incorporated food, bacteria, medication, temperature variations, fluids or solids, quantities, etc., environment, not only on the orifices but also on the entire visceral "in-between."

8. The first actions and subsequent reactions of the infant establish a transactional feed-back relationship of mother and child first *within them* as a symbiotic unit, later *between them* as foci. The mother utilizes her own developmental personality derivatives, her ethnic tradition and the current cultural values.

9. The environmental stimuli, acting on the undifferentiated whole organism, affect the subsequent differentiated parts. One of these is the visceral nervous system and its organ innervations, another the psychological system. Each later develops according to its natural maturational processes and receives further individual modification by special environmental influences.

10. Special influences acting on the organism, undifferentiated or in the process of differentiation through a variety of negative and positive conditioning processes, establish asymmetrical loading of developing smaller systems and create a variety of types of integration varying in degrees of capacity for strain under stress.

11. The later development of the psychological system, accompanying neocortical functioning, object relationship, learning by cathexis and the formation of word symbols, screens or reacts more or less successfully

against the imprint of the earliest experiences, memory traces and primary affects.

12. Regression (disintegration) under transactional stress produces revival of global functions with the recrudescence of primary affects expressed in primitive visceral fashion. Hence, investigation and treatment of the primary psychosomatic (healthy or disturbed) functions must revive the preverbal visceral undifferentiated total functions in which are contained the rudiments of both the organ and psychological systems.

13. The stresses which reëvoke inhibited fragments of visceral patterns and finally the total psychosomatic responses may be external, internal, somatic or psychological and traumatic or chronological (aging).

IX

Methods of research represent the operational genius of the investigator and cannot be devised apart from the subject matter and the material of the research. But there are certain generalities which can be expressed if our conceptual schemes are broad enough and our scientific models explicit.

We cannot operate alone anymore in a single field, whether this be biochemistry, physiology, psychology, neurology, internal medicine or psychoanalysis. We may observe with our own methods the workings of the system for which these are applicable and attempt to draw a boundary beyond which we cannot go. Our best vantage point is at the link or bridge between one system and another, but even here we cannot look in more than one direction at a time, nor do we have the capacity for exact observation of more than one system.

We are forced to work in an interdisciplinary group molded together by common conceptual schemes and scientific approaches. Such groups are rare and difficult to initiate. They are integrated into a workable and working team with the greatest of difficulty. The whole group must be subjected to lengthy and repetitive educational processes by its members through theoretical discussion and practice-runs on experimental data. Here is the need of psychosomatic research in our time. One need only look at the so-called correlations made by physiologists on the one hand and psychoanalysts on the other, each one working alone to determine the reason for this need. The group method is time consuming, costly, and not generously supported by foundations or public agencies who are mostly interested in projects rather than programs.

The assumptions and hypotheses which I have listed do not exclude investigations by any technique, of any age group nor of any dysfunction. However, they imply the utilization of a multidisciplinary attack using many exact techniques of measurement beginning with neo-natal organisms and their human and physical environments through years. The focus of the research on the internal aspects of differentiation, visceral learning, conditioning processes, system transactions and individuation, require special methods of measurement of visceral activities at rest and under stress. These physiological and biochemical methods are available but need application under controlled simultaneous observation of several systems by a variety of coöperating investigators. Data from such an approach will give us clues as to primary psychosomatic unity and subsequent specific somatic and psychological variations of function known as health or disease.

BIBLIOGRAPHY

1. ALEXANDER, F.: *Psychosomatic Medicine*. Norton, New York, 1950.
2. BENEDEK, T.: The Psychosomatic Implications of the Primary Unit: Mother-Child. *Am. J. Orthopsychiat.*, *19*:642, 1949.
3. BENEDEK, T.: On the Organizations of Psychic Energy: Instincts, Drives and Affects, Chapter V, in *Mid-Century Psychiatry*, ed. R. Grinker. Thomas, Springfield, 1952.
4. BINGER, C.: On So-Called Psychogenic Influences in Essential Hypertension. *Psychosom. Med.*, *13*:273, 1951.
5. CARMICHAEL, L.: *Manual of Child Psychology*. Wiley, New York, 1946.
6. DUNBAR, H. F.: *Psychosomatic Diagnosis*. Hoeber, New York, 1943.
7. ERIKSON, E. H.: Childhood and Society. Norton, New York, 1950.
8. FREUD, S.: *Three Contributions to the Theory of Sex*. Nervous and Mental Disease Monographs, New York, 1910.
9. GESELL, A., and ARMATRUDA, C. A.: *Developmental Diagnosis*. Hoeber, New York, 1941.
10. GREENACRE, P.: The Biological Economy of Birth. *The Psycho-analytic Study of the Child*, *1*:31. International Universities Press, New York, 1945.
11. GRINKER, R. R., and SPIEGEL, J. P.: *Men Under Stress*. Blakiston, Philadelphia, 1945.
12. HALLIDAY, J. L.: *Psychosocial Medicine: A Study of the Sick Society*. Norton, New York, 1948.
13. HERRICK, C. J.: *George E. Coghill, Naturalist and Philosopher*. University of Chicago Press, Chicago, 1949.
14. KEPECS, J., and ROBIN, M.: Relationship Between Certain Emotional States and Exudation into the Skin. *Psychosom. Med.*, *13*:1, 1951.
15. MARGOLIN, S.: Psychoanalysis and the Dynamics of Psychosomatic Medicine. 1952 (to be published).
16. SPIEGEL, J. P.: The Use of the Field Concept in the Analysis of Human Behavior (to be published).
17. WOLFF, H. G.: Life Stress and Bodily Disease—A Formulation. *Proc. ARNMD*, *29*:1059, 1950.

THE PROBLEM OF SPECIFICITY IN THE PSYCHOSOMATIC PROCESS

Lawrence S. Kubie, M.D.[1]

In considering the problem of specificity in psychosomatic relationships, it may be helpful to keep in mind certain steps through which medical science has moved in the understanding of disease in general. Under the influences of gross pathology, individual organs were once looked upon as the site of discrete and independent disease processes; then the tissues (Bichat); then the individual cell and its membranes (Virchow); until finally, all of these were seen to be mere nodal points in an incessant flux of biochemical and biophysical processes which of necessity involved not the tissues alone, but also all body fluids (Lewin and Kubie, 5). This is the biochemistry and the biophysics of disease, as it is understood today. The course of progress has thus been toward a pathodynamics of disease in the whole body, which selects only secondarily one or another organ for special emphasis. Therefore to approach the problem of specificity in psychosomatic medicine by reverting to a concept of organ disease in the study of psychodynamic relationships is a regression, which

[1] Clinical Professor of Psychiatry, Yale University School of Medicine; Faculty, New York Psychoanalytic Institute.

results in part from the fact that certain organs are sharply singled out psychologically, even when their physiological functions are not sharply segregated. Thus, organs which are merged physiologically into an indivisible whole can play multiple and complex roles in our conscious and unconscious mental processes: and the same organ can be at once both within and without the limiting boundaries of an individual's *I* world. For instance, when a colleague's four-year-old grandchild, struggling to urinate through an erect penis, looked down at himself and said, "Lie down, you know the rules," whom was he addressing?

This illustrates the multiplicity of the roles played by those organs from which we can receive discriminating afferent information. And it is this which makes possible what Margolin calls, "the illusion of function." And it is this which in our psychosomatic theorizing may find expression in the return to an organ concept.

With this general principle in mind, I wrote an article in 1944 (*1*) outlining a possible basis of classification of disorders from a psychosomatic standpoint. In this article I grouped the body involvement in mental conflicts under four categories—according to whether the organs chosen were those which implement (a) our relations to the outside world, (b) our instinctual functions, (c) our internal economy, or (d) a more diffuse body image as a whole. I believe that these suggestions may ultimately prove to have some value in relation to the problem of specificity when they are explored further. In the first group (a) the primary functions of the organ are innervated predominantly by the somatomuscular and somatosensory systems, with the autonomic system playing only a secondary supportive role. In the second group (b) the primary functions are initiated under the guidance of the voluntary nervous system with the autonomic nervous system taking over the more automatic secondary steps of these functions. In the third group (c) the autonomic nervous system functions almost alone. And in the fourth group (d) the somatosensory and the higher conceptual and symbolic systems play the primary role.

Classification of some sort is essential for any considerations of specificity. These suggestions may provide us with a useful approach to the problem of classification from the point of view of the neurophysiological mechanisms which are predominantly involved. To be complete, however, this would have to be integrated and correlated with a classification based on considerations of the dominant conscious and unconscious psychological mechanisms. This paper will deal largely with certain general principles of these psychological mechanisms.

I want first, however, to review briefly the history of the ontogenetic approach to the problem of specificity in psychopathological phenomena in general. In essence this consists of an effort to trace the life histories of individuals who ultimately develop specific neuroses, psychoses, or psychosomatic illnesses. It is the "how do they get that way?" approach. In the recent history of psychiatry this has taken three major forms:

(a) The orthodox Kraepelinian psychiatrist limited himself to a history of the development of a patient's symptoms;

(b) The Meyerian psychobiologist, and in some

measure Bleuler as well, went beyond this to gather a more intimate anamnesis; still based primarily, however, on data from a patient's conscious memories of his life. Here the attempt was to understand illness by correlating the evolution of the frank symptoms of illness with the development of the personality and of the general capacity to adjust to outer stresses. This was an important advance, in that it recognized the essential continuity of the forces which produce personality with those which produce symptoms. It carried the further implication that one cannot permanently modify symptoms without understanding and modifying the personality that lies behind them. Unfortunately instead of developing this lead fully, Meyer tended to take a somewhat moralistic attitude toward personality deviations. The personality was "blamed" for illness, and the patient was "blamed" for his personality and for his "habits." Habits were bad. Habits had to be changed, etc. Thus in practice the psychobiological approach tended to become a moralizing habit psychology, which circumscribed its scientific and therapeutic usefulness.

(c) The psychoanalytic contribution to the onto-genetic understanding of illness has added an essential link; i.e., the effort to trace the evolution of the unconscious components of personality. In psychoanalysis this has taken various different forms. The early emphasis was on the persistent traces of the so-called polymorphous perverse trends of infancy, which in turn was linked to the concept of specific erotogenic zones. Subsequently this was elaborated into the concepts of instinctual and libidinal development. Then with the formulation of our metapsychological metaphors came the effort to trace the separate yet intertwining development of three component parts of the personality (ego, superego, and id), operating in an incessant flux of fixations, regressions, identifications, incorporations, defenses, etc. So complex has this story become that we may be in some danger of losing our way in a verbal jungle; and in our wanderings through this jungle we sometimes comfort ourselves with metapsychological clichés to prove that we are not lost. Nevertheless there can be no doubt that this approach is important to an understanding of the ontogeny of illness.

Whatever the value of specific forms of ontogenetic explanations, we must face the fact that it is impossible to apply any of it with precision until we have settled at least two basic questions, which underlie the problem of the choice of a neurosis: (1) What are the dynamic units of illness whose ontogeny we are attempting to trace, and for which it may be legitimate to expect to find constant causal sequences? (2) At what point in their complex developmental stories do specific differentiating forces begin to operate; i.e., those forces which determine the final shape of illness?

However, before we consider these questions as they relate to the neurotic distortion of body function, it is necessary to consider them with respect to neuroses in general. Is any simple neurotic symptom reducible to a single and constant group of determinants?

I want to begin by suggesting that most neurotic symptoms may best be thought of as something, which, like a fever, can be produced in more than one way. True, there must be a final common pathway to each; but the approach to this final pathway may follow many different routes. In climbing a mountain, several faces can often be scaled. Along each face the ascent will be remarkably different. Yet as the various paths converge on the top, there will be some path up the final peak which is common to all. This may be the case for even the simplest neurotic symptom. I do not assume that this is necessarily the case. Perhaps there is one path which is unique from the base to the peak; but many considerations make this improbable. At least we must always keep in mind the possibility and perhaps even the probability that specific determinants of specific neurotic symptoms may arise toward the end rather than the beginning of the causal chain.

It seems to me that this was Freud's tacit assumption throughout the early years of his work. But the introduction of such concepts as anal, oral, urethral, and pregenital characters (i.e., the attempt to link character traits to the "erogenous zones" and to early phases of instinctual development) led automatically to parallel efforts to link neurotic symptoms and syndromes to the same early events. Paradoxical though this seems, we may discover that the more general aspects of personality and character are in fact quite closely related to the more universal and basic alternatives among the early instinctual events; whereas the specificity of neurotic symptoms and syndromes may have later or at least more accidental and individual determinants. As I will indicate below, my clinical experience inclines me at present to this view in connection with the neuroses in general, as well as their somatic involvements.

Furthermore, the more deeply I study my own patients as the years go on, the more convinced do I become that we do not yet know what are the essential dynamic units of the neurotic process in general. We have been misled by our fascination with bizarre symptoms into looking upon symptoms and symptom clusters as entities. This has led us directly to base our causal theories on the tacit assumption that the roots and meanings of each such symptom or cluster must be constant. Yet there is no convincing evidence that there are not many ways of developing a handwashing compulsion, many ways of developing a height phobia, indeed many ways of developing any of the neurotic symptoms or states which one might call to mind. Moreover, it seems clear from everyday clinical experience that this same height phobia or handwashing compulsion can arise in extraordinarily varied psychopathological soils. Many kinds of sick personality can voice the identical complaint; just as many different kinds of illness can have a rash or a temperature or a swollen liver. This is one of the concrete clinical observations which make it seem likely that the common path to the specific symptom may occur only as a late element in the long chain of individually nonspecific, inadequate events and forces.

If this should prove to be true for the run-of-the-mill manifestations of the neurotic process, then certainly we would hardly expect to find it otherwise for the trains of genetic events which end up in a psychosomatic disturbance. After all, a large number of additional variables enter into the production of psychosomatic disorders over and above those which shape the ordinary neurosis. Merely to list these additional variables will emphasize the likelihood that it is unrealistic to expect a simple unitary specificity. In short, here in the brief history of psychosomatic theory we find another example of that ancient search for the single answer, which has misled medical research so often in the past.

Without attempting an exhaustive catalogue of these variables, I will give examples of a few of the more important. Among these I will mention first the occurrence of organic disease or injury in the patient himself. These in turn vary as to nature, severity, and age. One patient in his first months had an intractable skin condition which was treated by wrapping him literally in cotton wool and by immobilizing him for months. Another patient had a similar skin condition; but it occurred during the later phallic phase, continuing into the early oedipal period. He was treated by a nudist technique. That is, he was encouraged to run naked indoors and outdoors, under all circumstances, and at every opportunity. In a third patient the skin condition involved primarily the eyes, and in a fourth the perineum. It will be obvious that the psychological consequences had to be different.

Add to these differences certain others: as for instance, those arising from the fact that scratching can in one instance be a gnawing pleasurable experience, in another purely painful. In a third, scratching has a masturbatory implication, with its subsequent guilt and fear. Furthermore, for every early experience of continued pain and discomfort the psychological consequences will differ, depending upon whether the discomfort is continuous or episodic, with a constant undertone of fear of recurrences.

Again, in considering the aftereffects of prior experience of illness, we must include the variability in various aspects of treatment, and also in the emotional atmosphere which attended treatment. Was the treatment effective or ineffective, comforting or painful, prompt or slow? Did adults react to the child's distress with guilt and irritation and anger and tension, generating similar feelings in the child, out of which deeply buried resentment and grievance may grow? Or did the parents treat the child with tender loving care, perhaps even to excess, so that the early experience of illness acquired an exaggerated secondary gain? Did the injury or illness evoke merely fantasies of mutilation and incapacity or actual mutilation and incapacity? Polio in one child meant a long period of total immobility and dependence, and in another a mild transient weakness of one extremity. One child compensated by clinging; another overcompensated by exaggerated gestures of defiant independence. One exploited an injured member, another denied it, so that the injured part of the body became an hysterically dissociated, alien, or foreign body in the I-structure. Clearly not even the simplest experience of illness or injury can always mean one thing.

I have alluded in passing to the variable extent to which the adult world can effectively come to the child's help in moments of distress. Consider early asthma, as a particularly poignant example. Probably few experiences can come to a small child which are as devastating. Breathing is linked to the most primitive roots of fear. In the midst of an asthmatic bout, what then must a child feel toward the adults who stand helpless around him, breathing freely themselves, yet unable to bring him significant easement? How do we

71

as scientists determine whether the psychic structure which evolves has a causal relationship to that asthma or is its consequence? And can the relationship be the same in an asthma which starts only later in life?

This brings to mind still another basic variable: namely, the qualitative and quantitative differences in the guilt and terror which are associated with the different bodily processes and needs: e.g., breathing, eating, defecating, excreting, sex, etc. In another place (2) I have pointed to some of the inevitable differences in the psychological structures which are built around the basic organic processes. These differences constitute the nucleus around which cluster the effects of many other variable experiences, such as separation from the mother or father. Here again early physiological functions can be influenced, the influence depending upon the quality of the relationship which has preceded the separation, the duration of the separation (Spitz, 7), and the fears and the guilts which are generated before, during, and after the separation. In turn all of these play on the later disturbance of functions which can arise.

To these many variables which cluster around the bodily experiences of the patient himself, we must add those which occur as vicarious experiences; i.e., through accidents, injuries, illnesses, and deaths which occur not to the patient himself, but to those with whom he has emotionally significant relationships. Here are felt the influences of both positive and hostile identifications, the influences of guilt at being free from pain and disability where the relationship has been hostile, and also where the relationship is loving. Here again we see in the child the influence of discovering that adults are vulnerable, which carries the threat: "As I grow up, I too will become vulnerable." These are only some of the variables which enter into the formation of psychosomatic disorders through the illnesses of others in the child's environment.

As though all of this were not enough, we must also bear it in mind that disability, disturbances in function, and mutilations have a chain of consequences which arise through their symbolic implications on three psychic levels; i.e., the realistic or conscious level; the preconscious; and the deeper, symbolic or unconscious level. This brings three more groups of variables into the picture, making it impossible for any illness or trauma, however simple it may be intrinsically, ever to have only one universal implication. Even when a broken leg occurs to two children of the same sex and at the same age and in the same way, it will introduce a complex mixture of universal and individualized conscious and unconscious implications into subsequent personality distortions, into subsequent neurotic developments, and into later disturbances of physiological function.

In connection with all of the experimental work on diseased organs we have always to remind ourselves of the difficulty of determining whether the disease or injury has brought in its train an array of secondary psychological and physiological consequences which distort the function of that organ. In this respect most of the work on patients with gastrostomies is faulty, with the one striking exception of the work by Dr. Sydney Margolin (6) and his associates. Let me quote from the discussion of that paper (3):

"We must estimate what it means to a human being to have a gastrostomy for four years as in this case, and in some other reported cases for much longer. Inevitably any such dramatic and distressing condition must come to occupy a central position in the patient's emotional life. This consideration makes one hesitate to accept at face value some of the earlier descriptions of gastric physiology, such as those of Carlson and of Wolf and Wolff, none of which takes into account the pathological inflation or distortion of the emotional correlations of a mutilated organ. The mutilated organ becomes the primary organ for the expression of everything that the patient thinks and feels, consciously and unconsciously. We have no right to assume that under these circumstances, the responses of a gastrostomy patient will represent the gastric functions of an intact human being, without exaggeration or distortions or both."

This caution applies equally to the data from all such organic injuries, for both organic and symbolic reasons.

These variations in the symbolic meanings of illness are among the subtlest and the most inconstant of all the variable forces which are at work in determining the ultimate psychosomatic picture. It should be unnecessary to mention this here; yet strangely enough, even in much analytic theory there is a tacit assumption that there is a one-to-one relationship between a concept and its symbol. This, of course, is never true on any level. There is not a simple relationship even between a *table* as a real object, and the concept *table,* or its verbal symbol. A table is a place to sit at, to eat from, to write on, to hammer on, to meet around, to put books and magazines on. A table is also a group of figures in a column. One tables a resolution. A table is a breast; a home; a mother; etc., etc. Since this is true on conscious and preconscious levels, inevitably it is true on unconscious levels of symbolic function as well. To imagine anything else would be curiously unrealistic, since we encounter the same multivalence of symbols in every dream that we analyze. A patient with a sore tongue dreamed of wanting a piece of cold ham or hot tongue. The hot tongue meant the tongue lashing she wanted to give her husband and analyst. It meant the "tonguing" she expected in the analysis. It meant the tongue as a substitute for the genital intercourse of which her husband's impotence deprived her. It meant her old dependent infantile relationship to her mother. It meant the threat of punishment and death through the fantasy of a cancer of the tongue. Here it meant an identification with Freud, in a megalomanic fulfillment of dreams of omniscience and omnipotence. In addition, there was the fact that the tongue actually was sore, which on this particular night played a part in the choice of the tongue to represent all of these struggles.

Another group of variable forces may operate through the hypothetical influence of some degree of organ compliance or of local susceptibility. Much is made of this in speculative writings about the dynamics of specific symptoms. Yet it has never been thoroughly or adequately explored. The lack is understandable when we consider the great difficulty of subjecting it to objective investigations. The difficulty is how to know which came first. The existence of a correlation between physiological process A and symptom B always makes it possible that a causal relationship between the two may exist; but it never proves whether A caused B, or whether B caused A, or whether the two arose concurrently from a common cause. In a recent study by J. I. Lacey (4), the investigators recorded physiological variations in children, who will be followed through coming years for their subsequent somatic and psychological histories. The psychological approach was not as sophisticated as one might wish: and ultimately a more penetrating study will be needed of unconscious as well as conscious factors in the personalities of such children. However, it will be of interest to see what types of psychosomatic disturbances may develop in any of these children. Another study which accepts the same predictive challenge is being carried on at the Johns Hopkins Medical School. All medical students are now subjected to an intensive psychological scrutiny; and through the coming years these doctors-to-be will send back to the study group physiological data on their own blood pressures, pulse rates, etc. In time it should be possible to see whether from the current psychological material alone predictions could have been made as to which of these students would first develop cardiovascular or other physiological disturbances in subsequent years. When complete, this study should be a helpful contribution to the problem of specificity, especially if by studying the dreams, free associations, and fantasies of these medical students the unconscious as well as conscious levels of their psychic structures are investigated.

Let me return to one further consequence of the multiple implications of all units of symbolic function, whether of an organism as a whole or of its part functions. This is equally true for normal function. There is literally nothing that we can do that does not serve multiple purposes on all levels, conscious, preconscious, and unconscious. This is true of exercise and sleep, of waiting or moving, of eating, drinking, and intercourse, of reading a book, or delivering a lecture. Is it conceivable then that any pathological disturbance in function will not serve multiple purposes to an equal extent? It is possible, of course, that to the degree to which any physiological function comes under the domination of purposes which are preponderantly unconscious its functioning will become limited, restricted, and stereotyped. If we know anything at all about the neurotic process, this must surely occur. This does not mean, however, that the functional restrictions and the stereotypes imposed by the domination of unconscious processes will be identical for all individuals, nor that the restricted function will not have multiple symbolic connotations. Quite on the contrary, one would expect a stereotype of function out of a multiplicity of unconscious purposes for each individual, which would bear an imprint of that individual's personality and his problems. Thus the choice of the organ and of the functional disturbance will be dependent upon multiple factors, some of which are essentially accidental in the final path to that particular symptom.

What then of the concept of specific personality types

and personality profiles? According to certain workers these personality types may best be characterized in terms of one or two dominant traits; or according to other workers as a mosaic of traits which make up a "profile." I find it difficult today to accept either school of thought. When these hypotheses and their data were first put forward, I welcomed them with eagerness; but as the years have gone by I have found it increasingly difficult to reconcile these points of view with my clinical observations and my theoretical development. Also, as I go over their material now I find myself troubled by certain obscurities both in theory and in data which did not impress me at first. I am never quite clear when they are talking about conscious, preconscious, or unconscious personality trends, life stresses, and conflicts. Nor is it always possible to know whether they are talking about primary trends in an hypothetical personality type, or those which are overcompensatory defenses. Thus when they talk about dependency needs, I cannot be sure whether they are thinking of dependency as a reaction formation against a primary unconscious aggressivity, or of aggressivity as the reaction formation with dependency as the primary need. This is a type of obscurity in clinical descriptions which has made it difficult to check their correlations.

So much for the logic of not expecting specificity. There is also much positive evidence against it. On several occasions I have gathered together for clinical demonstration a group of clinically identical disorders: e.g., groups of migraines, of ulcerative colitis, of cardiospasms, etc. On such occasions I have been impressed by the dissimilarities at least as vividly as by the similarities among the individuals in each clinical group. Indeed I could not convince myself that the similarities were greater than those which obtain among any heterogenous group of neurotic patients. To that I add a fact that is well known to all of us: namely, that as one explores deeply in any analysis, one comes to certain common origins of the neurotic process, whereupon seemingly sharp differences in the symptoms with which the patient has presented himself appear to be relatively superficial vagaries superimposed on the more constant underlying neurotic process. Thus in the course of time most analysts come to feel that the neurotic process is remarkably constant, while the neurotic symptom is as variable as is the dream symbol. In dreams we take it for granted that the patient may represent his deepest problems in an extraordinarily wide variety of symbols; and also that in that patient the same symbol can be used to represent many unconscious problems. I have gradually come to feel that an equally wide variety is possible for neurotic symptoms in general, and for psychosomatic disturbances in particular. This point receives further substantiation from the fact that in different phases the same patient may represent his problems in psychosomatic constellations which are wholly different from one another. In one patient an ulcerative colitis was replaced by a severe dermatitis which in turn was replaced by a severe migraine, all of them finally being replaced by a psychotic break.

Under these circumstances it would seem that the quest for uniform specificity in psychosomatic disorders arises out of a fallacious assumption about the specificity of the dynamic sequences in the etiology of the neuroses in general.

These various considerations bring me back to my basic questions:

(1) What in general are the indivisible dynamic units in the neurotic process?

(2) At what point in the chain of events do specific determinants become operative?

(3) Finally, how does the psychosomatic process as such arise? Why does the effort to solve an unconscious conflict ever turn in the bodily direction?

Until we can answer this third question, it is unlikely that we will find specific factors for specific types of psychosomatic dysfunction. All efforts to answer this last question emphasize the importance of a dissociative and psychologically regressive movement, regressive either chronologically to an earlier age, or regressive with respect to the type of controlling mechanisms used, or to the type of needs experienced, or to the type of compromise adjustments which are employed in expressing those needs. But regressive and dissociative processes occur in the course of the decompensations which occur when any latent neurotic process becomes manifest. Our question, therefore, has to be more precisely asked: what is there which is of a peculiar, or special or different or specific nature about the regressive and dissociative processes which results in physiological disturbances? I believe that this question should be our starting point. But I can only ask this question: I cannot answer it.

BIBLIOGRAPHY

1. KUBIE, L. S.: The Basis of a Classification of Disorders from the Psychosomatic Standpoint. *Bull. N. Y. Acad. Med., 20*:46-65, 1944.
2. KUBIE, L. S.: Instincts and Homeostasis. *Psychosom. Med., 10*:15-30, 1948; and in *The Yearbook of Psychoanalysis, 5*:157-188. International Universities Press, New York, 1949.
3. KUBIE, L. S.: Review and Discussion: "The Behavior of the Stomach During Psychoanalysis," by Margolin, S. J. *Psa. Quart., 20*: 369-372, 1951.
4. LACEY, J. L.: An Experimental Study of Differential Somatic Emphasis on Stress Responses. *Psychosom. Med.* (in press).
5. LEWIN, B. D., and KUBIE, L. S.: 1801-1951: Mankind Discovers Man. *New York Evening Post 150th Anniversary Edition.* November 12, 1951, pp. 33-34.
6. MARGOLIN, S. J.: The Behavior of the Stomach During Psychoanalysis. *Psa. Quart., 20*:349-368, 1951.
7. SPITZ, R. A.: Anaclitic Depression. *The Psychoanalytic Study of the Child, 2*:313-343. International Universities Press, New York, 1946.

GENESIS OF PSYCHOSOMATIC SYMPTOMS IN INFANCY

The Influence of Infantile Traumata upon
Symptom Choice

MARGARET W. GERARD, Ph.D., M.D.[1]

As research emphasis has been placed increasingly
upon the influence of pregenital experiences in symptom
and character development, it has become evident that in
the early months of life, the framework for later development is set down. In this period, the child's physical
incapacity makes him completely dependent upon the
environment for the wherewithal of survival as well as
for pleasure and pain experiences. This early environment consists, mainly, of a mother or her surrogate. The
dependency of the baby upon the mother or nurse and
a reciprocal need of the mother for satisfactions from
the child, Benedek has described as a symbiosis (2).

Within this symbiotic relationship, the child develops
habits of expectation and reaction, which adapt him to
the conditions in which he finds himself, and defend
him against noxious and unpleasant experiences. These
early habits one may consider as the first stages in the

[1] From the Institute for Psychoanalysis, Chicago, and the Depart-
ment of Psychiatry, University of Illinois, Chicago.

development of what Hartmann names the "conflict-less" ego (6), a step beyond the simple neurological reflex response to stimuli. Adequate motherliness offers a healthy environment in which the adaptive tasks remain within the infant's capacity and the ego habits become those which keep the infant physically comfortable in a maximum and acceptable relationship to the environment. Lack of motherliness increases the difficulties of the adaptive tasks, in various ways. Spitz has shown, dramatically, how infant neglect produces "affect hunger" which then turns the infant away from the environment into autistic habits of body need and pleasure seeking, so-called anaclitic depression (14). Hartmann has discussed the influence of a mother's restraint of her infant upon the development of his hostile feelings and responses (7). Bergman and Escalona claim that insufficient protection of the infant from stimuli develop childhood psychosis (3).

Since early adaptation is mainly that of adjustment of the various body organs to their various functions in extrauterine conditions, it is reasonable to suspect that later maladaptation of the organ due to emotional causes may arise from emotional difficulties experienced in the first months of life when patterns of response are initiated (9).

The possibility that such a premise was tenable seemed to be substantiated by the fact that where histories of psychosomatic cases included information concerning the relation of the mother to the patient in infancy, the relationship always was fraught with various traumatic experiences, such as rejection, cruelty, neglect, inconsistency, unprotected separations and the like, which would produce actual physical suffering in the child. That this suffering may be more intense in the infant than in the older child, and therefore offer greater emotional traumatizing, is suggested by experimental findings of Mirsky (10) which suggest that at least some sensory thresholds in the infant are practically nil. Also, Freud's comment that the *Reizschutz* (or protection against stimuli) is a function of the ego would indicate that the pre-ego period, i.e., early infancy, is one with inadequate protection against stimuli. Therefore, with lack of both a threshold to stimuli and of adequate protection against noxious ones, excess organ pains would, conceivably, initiate excessive protective reflex responses, sensitizing, then, one organ system over another. The localization of sensitivity in an organ system which had been exposed to suffering, such that a psychosomatic disorder later developed in that system under emotional stress, has been suggested by Deutsch (4). It would follow Fenichel's hypothesis that an event is traumatic because it stirs an unconscious conflict—or, in other terms, revives old unresolved suffering (5). In addition, it is possible that the psychosomatic symptoms may follow Seitz' theory that psychogenic symptoms take on the character of the difficulties arising in the original conflict situation (13). Thus, a somatic symptom echoes a somatic disorder which was unmastered. My own tentative theory which, for validation, needs more clinical evidence to support it,* is that the localiza-

* Through the support of a grant from the Field Foundation, further investigations into the details of postpartum maternal-child relationships in cases of childhood psychosomatic disorders are in progress.

tion of organ pathology may represent only an exacerbation of a chronic condition which started in infancy but was masked for years or months until precipitating causes produced a flare-up. The condition might be compared to infections which are chronic but become acute when some body insult lowers resistance; dysentery, nephritis, appendicitis and the like.

A first attempt to correlate infantile experiences with somatic disorders was made recently by Spitz (15) when he classified the characters of the mothers of the infants presenting certain psychogenic disorders. For instance, he stated that the mothers of babies with three-month colic were primarily anxious and overpermissive; of babies with infantile neurodermatitis, were hostile under the garb of anxiousness; of babies with coma of newborn, were primarily overtly rejecting.

I became interested, several years ago, in studying and analyzing detailed behavior of mothers in the care of their children in an attempt to determine the influence upon ego development of minute variations in the mode of feeding, of holding, of supporting, of bathing, of talking or singing, of smiling or frowning, etc. The study also included securing information to assess the influence of the consistency or lack of consistency of these actions; and of the influence of exposure to completely different modes of behavior, which produce the "separation trauma" described by Anna Freud, when a mother substitute displaces the original mother or nurse. It seemed to me that from such data might one find the answer to questions of choice of symptoms and of personality characteristics which have evaded explanation from gross descriptions of environmental experiences and which have led perhaps too often to the answer of constitutional causality or causal nihilism. If, as Margaret Mead (8) suggests, cultural trends are communicated and taught to infants by the mother's tone of voice, mode of handling, etc., is it not possible that varying behavior of mothers within a single culture could produce varying responses in their infants?

For this present paper, I have separated from the total study of maternal behavior those cases in which various psychosomatic symptoms occurred as elements in the total neurotic constellation or personality of the children. Several of the cases were analyzed by me or by students under my supervision; the rest of the cases are those presented in the child psychosomatic seminar at the University of Illinois. These cases were studied conjointly by a child psychoanalyst and a psychoanalytically trained pediatrician; in most instances during hospitalization on the children's ward as well as in outpatient clinic after hospitalization, histories were taken on each case from three angles, pediatric, psychiatric, and social workers', and from both parents or other adults caring for the child. Detailed exploration of the first months of life was emphasized, and chronological sequence of events was followed in the infants. Actual present behavior of the mother was observed and reported. Psychological examinations including Rorschach and CAT or TAT were done on all cases if the child was old enough to respond.

There are thirty-eight cases in all, all under twelve years of age, of which there are eight ulcerative colitis, nine coeliac disease or megalocolon with encopresis (diagnosis varied according to condition of stools but

86

all showed X-ray redundancy of intestinal tract with spasm at varying spots and at various times), three duodenal ulcer, one pylorospasm, five asthma, three eczema, one rheumatoid arthritis, two diabetes, five obesity, one hyperthyroid. The preponderance of gastrointestinal cases represented clinical interest rather than preponderance of clinic intake. For statistical validity, this number is meager indeed, and any generalizations must be most tentative. However, in those disorders of five or more cases, consistency in findings relative to maternal behavior and attitudes are most suggestive that there are correlations between specific maternal behavior and attitudes to the child and to specific organ function, which affect the functioning of those organs in infancy and may sensitize the organs so that their malfunctioning becomes one facet in the total neurotic mosaic.

I do not wish to discuss here all the facets of the study, but let me say that much interesting confirming information was unearthed in the cases. Although the total constellation of the neuroses and personality patterns varied considerably from case to case, the secondary neurotic symptoms and personality characteristics were consistent with developmental expectation when one considered the influence upon the early neurosis of later occurring traumata and experiences in the anal, oedipal and latency periods.

Before detailed data are gone into, I would like to mention an important general characteristic which all these cases had in common with each other and with all the cases in the study which presented various psychotic-like symptoms. With no exception, all these mothers were narcissistic and uninterested in the child except as a self-enhancing asset. They resented the exertion involved in child care and rarely gained pleasure from the mother-child relationship. In other words, they all lacked mature motherliness. In addition as we shall find, most were rejecting and physically cruel in various ways and resented the added care of the infant during physical illness. Therefore, each child presenting a psychosomatic disorder had experienced frustrated dependence at a stage when body needs are dependent upon the mother for satisfaction.

Although both mother and child were studied quite extensively in each of the cases I am to speak of, I intend to lift out of context only specific attitudes and behavior activities of the mothers which seemed to us in each case to create an environment which insulted the infant organism, but which were particularly noxious to the specific functioning of certain organs.

The preponderance of gastrointestinal cases occurred because of a focus upon these cases at the time of study. Other cases in other areas are under study now. Groups in which only one or very few cases have been studied in detail are mentioned, merely to indicate the trends which we have seen, but which must be confirmed or disproved by further data.

I. *The cases of ulcerative colitis,* five male and three female, were all unwanted children. The mothers complained of disgust and dislike of stools and diaper changes and were particularly irritated with the child's diarrhea. Bowel training in all cases had been early and punitive.

In character these mothers were dependent upon

their own mothers; four of them housed their mothers in their own homes. They were unloving; six of them being sexually frigid; but were very ambitious for the child's achievement of training, walking, talking, and pushed for independent but conforming behavior.

II. *The cases of coeliac disease and megalocolon* (with or without encopresis), consisting of eleven males and six females, possessed the most disturbed of all mothers studied. Eight were psychotic with depressive and apathetic behavior interrupted by occasional violent outbursts. The others were withdrawn, complaining and irritable.

Severe reaction to constipation was described by them. It elicited anger, irritation and frequent enemas and suppositories, often used preventively when the infant was not constipated.

None of these babies were breast fed; most were fed with "propped" bottle rather than held, and most were "force fed" when disinterest in food was shown. All of the babies were exposed to further severe physical suffering from beating, slapping, yelling. In four cases the father was cruel, while the mother passively permitted his cruelty to the child.

III. *The duodenal ulcer cases*, three males, were exposed to irritable mothers who were particularly displeased with the extra care involved in illness, and all three babies had frequent illnesses (pneumonia, influenza, otitis media bronchitis, etc.). One mother, bringing her child who had vomited with an upper respiratory infection, said to the intern, "Please take him in and keep him!" However, she had severe death fears for the baby, calling the intern frequently to ask if he had died.

All three mothers were inconsistent; threatening, hugging, then scolding, shouting, spanking and often shaking the child at feeding if he dawdled or such. None of the babies were breast fed; none were held during bottle feeding; and all were on feeding routines with long intervals.

IV. *The asthma cases,* three male, two female, were mothered by dependent, demanding, ungiving mothers who in all cases were charming and socially wooing, presenting an external appearance of good adjustment.

Of particular importance may be their hypersensitiveness and irritability to the crying of the infant. Two said they "shook the baby out of crying"; another beat him; another said she left him alone until he stopped crying.

V. *The eczema cases,* three males, had mothers who were fearful and somewhat agitated. They did not handle the children much, but our three mothers were rough at times when they had to handle the babies. Spitz (15) reported similar findings in a study of neurodermatitis of mothers' attitudes toward their babies, except for the observation we made that the mothers were rough at times when handling was necessary. Two mothers had heart attacks and were in constant fear of their own death; also they were frequently absent from the children because of illness.

VI. *Obesity cases,* three male, two female, had obese mothers except for one. All the mothers were compulsive eaters and compulsive feeders, were overly concerned about the quantity of the babies' food intake, were oversolicitous, anxious and irritable at times of regurgitation or of food refusal.

VII. Two female *diabetes cases* were exposed to neglectful and irregular feedings from withdrawn mothers, both of whom were severely disturbed; one was later institutionalized as a paranoid psychosis; the other entered a depression when the baby was three months old, following the death of her own mother.

VIII. One female *rheumatoid arthritis* case had a mother who was compulsive, unemotional, perfectionistic (described by the social worker as Grant Woods "American Gothic"). She held the baby stiffly, and with a firmness which inhibited free movement. She never caressed the baby. When asked about it, she said, "Should one? Wouldn't it spoil her?"

IX. One female *hyperthyroid case* was an unwanted child of an anxious, trembly, fearful mother who was "afraid to break the baby" when caring for her. Much of the care was relegated to a ne'er-do-well, irresponsible, alcoholic father, a grandmother, an aunt, the mother-in-law, etc., while the mother worked.

Summary and Conclusions

The cases in this pilot study only offer hints as to possible biographical experiences which may play roles in the sensitizing of different organs or organ systems so that the organs break down in later life to exhibit physical pathology. I do not wish to imply that these particular factors represent the only determinants but merely that, in the multiplicity of determinants, these seem to play important parts. In no way do I believe the data to be full enough nor microscopically accurate enough to draw categorical conclusions. I only wish to pose possible theoretical implications.

John Rosen, in discussing the theory of his "direct analytic therapy" for schizophrenics, states that "a parent (normal or motherly) responds to a disturbance of a child by trying to relieve the disturbance. The narcissistic parent resents this disturbance and attacks the annoying aggressor (the child). The parental death-wish against the child may be perceived by the child's unconscious and constitute an 'unholy peril' with accompanying terrifying anxiety." This anxiety he believes may be the basis of the schizophrenia (12).

In the various psychosomatic cases related above, the children were exposed to anxiety and suffering at the hands of rejecting and narcissistic mothers, or of fate in the form of extraneous terrifying experiences, in much the same way schizophrenics have been exposed to suffering in childhood.

As suggested in the beginning, severe reactions may be expected to occur in response to severe suffering in early infancy because of a minimal *Reizschutz* to suffering. Why, then, did these children develop neurotic organic disorders and not schizophrenia? Schwartz and Semrad (16) in a recent publication state their belief that "psychosomatic disorders are in a sense a defense and protection against a psychotic break." Also, in certain psychosomatic disorders, as ulcerative colitis and duodenal ulcer, dangers of psychotic episodes developing during psychoanalysis has been discussed in the literature. Margolin in this symposium stated that certain psychosomatic symptoms may alternate with psychosis.

I do not presume to answer this question. However, I wonder if it is possible that the mothers of frank schizophrenics may not be more disturbed, more rejecting generally than those of our cases, so that more elements of adequate ego building are possible for those cases developing organ disorders than for schizophrenics.

Corroboration for the supposition of this possibility may be found in the fact that the ego of those psychosomatic cases studied presented more adequate adaptive capacity than cases of childhood psychosis. Except for the physical illnesses their adjustment to people, to work, to play, and such like, was neurotic but not psychotic, or atypical to the extent of the patients described by Rank (*11*). What this implies is that the total personality constellations of the psychosomatic cases, though pathological, presented the main defects in the integration of certain body functions into the total functioning.

Emphasis of focus of the mother's rejection upon particular physiological functioning in the early months may be the differential etiological feature between schizophrenia and psychosomatic disorders and between the specific different organ neurosis.

For instance, mothers of ulcerative colitis cases seem to reject and be especially irritated at the time of diarrheal bowel illness; mothers of coeliacs and megalocolon are irritated and anxious with constipation and thus impose enemas; of duodenal ulcers reject any feeding irregularities and dependencies; of pylorospasm resent feeding demand and control from child; of rheumatic arthritis react to the helplessness and the need to be held and supported, by rough handling, and so on.

The incapacity for adequate functioning and susceptibility to breakdown of an organ may stem from the injury of the organ induced by the mother's care of the child during the physiological functioning of that organ; injury due to mishandling and cruelty resulting from mother's rejection of both child and functioning, but increased rejection during specific functioning as in eating, defecating, crying. As I have said, it may be that a chronic disorder ensues showing only symptoms during exacerbations, or a reflex sensitivity may be imposed.

As all studies disclose, other neurotic symptoms and character conflicts exist in patients who also present organ symptoms. In many instances these conflicts are similar. The studies of Alexander et al. indicate that specific conflicts are specific for each psychosomatic illness (1).

It is possible that the conflict found specific for the disease is one produced by the same kinds of experience creating the somatic symptom or it may be possible that concomitant symptoms and conflicts are similar only when the mother's behaviors are alike in secondary ways causing similar total reactions. Since these mothers possess so many traumatizing characteristics which are repetitiously alike, one may explain the frequency of similarity.

In other words, the specific conflict may be a necessary part of the total syndrome or a usual concomitant similar to the description in *Kon-Tiki* of the sharks' course always being accompanied by many pilot fish.

One may assume that the pilot fish determine the course, or one may recognize only that they usually go along together, and may or may not have symbiotic or correlated meaning.

BIBLIOGRAPHY

1. ALEXANDER, F.: *Psychosomatic Medicine*. Norton, New York, 1950.
2. BENEDEK, T.: Adaptation to Reality in Early Infancy. *Psa. Quart.*, 7:200, 1938.
3. BERGMAN, P., and ESCALONA, S.: Unusual Sensitivities in Very Young Children. *The Psychoanalytic Study of the Child*, 3/4:333-352. International Universities Press, New York, 1949.
4. DEUTSCH, F.: The Choice of Organ in Organ Neuroses. *Int. J. Psa.*, 20:252, 1939.
5. FENICHEL, O.: *The Psychoanalytic Theory of Neurosis*. Norton, New York, 1945.
6. HARTMANN, H.: Psychoanalysis and Developmental Psychology. *The Psychoanalytic Study of the Child*, 5:7-17. International Universities Press, New York, 1950.
7. HARTMANN, H., KRIS, E., and LOEWENSTEIN, R. M.: Comments on the Formation of Psychic Structure. *The Psychoanalytic Study of the Child*, 2:11-38. International Universities Press, 1946.
8. MEAD, M.: Discussion. *Am. J. Orthopsychiat.*, 19:349, 1949.
9. MICHAELS, J.: A Psychiatric Adventure in Comparative Pathophysiology of the Infant and Adult. *J. Nerv. & Ment. Dis. 100*:49, 1944.
10. MIRSKY, I. A.: Personal communication.
11. RANK, B.: Aggression. *The Psychoanalytic Study of the Child*, 3/4:43-48. International Universities Press, New York, 1949.
12. ROSEN, J.: The Treatment of Schizophrenic Psychosis by Direct Analytic Therapy. *Psychiat. Quart.*, 21:3, 1947.
13. SEITZ, P. F. D.: Psychocutaneous Conditioning During the First Two Weeks of Life. *Psychosom. Med.*, 12:187, 1950.
14. SPITZ, R. A.: Anaclitic Depression. *The Psychoanalytic Study of the Child*, 2:313-342. International Universities Press, New York, 1946.
15. SPITZ, R. A.: The Psychogenic Diseases in Infancy. *The Psychoanalytic Study of the Child*, 6:255-275. International Universities Press, New York, 1951.
16. SCHWARTZ, J., and SEMRAD, E.: Psychosomatic Disorders in Psychoses. *Psychosom. Med.*, 13:314, 1951.

PROBLEMS OF THERAPY

M. RALPH KAUFMAN, M.D.[1]

The assignment to discuss problems of therapy within the framework of this symposium presents a challenge. It is realized that in order to have an adequate theory of therapy one must have a theory of illness. Psychoanalysis has such a theoretical frame of reference, with particular concepts in relation to the origin and meaning of the symptoms. Indeed, within this theoretical frame of reference the whole gamut of psychobiological functioning of the individual is included so that it is possible to set up a hypothetical spectrum which goes from the so-called normal to the most deeply regressed psychotic and which may include all psychophysiological or psychopathological phenomena. As psychoanalysts it is incumbent upon us to exploit our clinical and theoretical knowledge in relation to any problem that confronts us. This will enable us to understand what we already have knowledge about and also will bring us to the limitations in our knowledge; only in this way can we make further progress. We must be careful that the fascination of new observations in ancillary fields

[1] Psychiatrist to the Mount Sinai Hospital, New York City and Clinical Professor of Psychiatry, College of Physicians and Surgeons, Columbia University, New York City.

does not result in a jettisoning of what has already been won through the painstaking work of years.

Since this symposium is on "The Psychosomatic Concept in Psychoanalysis," it can only be hoped that by the end of it we shall have a clear-cut formulation which will place the so-called psychosomatic symptom in its proper biologically determined dynamic, economic, genetic and structural aspects. Recognizing the extraordinary complexity of the factors involved, it may nevertheless be relevant to discuss some of the possibilities in symptom formation. There is a certain danger in oversimplification, but what I would like to accomplish is the formulation of some basic principles rather than to present a series of clinical therapeutic problems. This is not only a review but an attempt at synthesis of our present knowledge in order to throw psychoanalytic light upon our practices. This is especially important in the therapies utilized in the so-called psychosomatic field.

It is generally accepted that symptom formation is a compromise, however achieved, between the conflicting forces within the personality, i.e., id, ego, superego, and to this must be added reality. What are the possibilities for somatic manifestations? We are, of course, familiar with the somatic phenomenon of conversion hysteria, even though Freud after a discussion of this problem stated, "Why the formation of symptoms in conversion-hysteria should be such a peculiarly obscure thing I do not know. But the fact provides us with a good reason for quitting such an unproductive field of inquiry" (13, p. 60). And this in an area which has perhaps been the most fertile and well studied in all of psychoanalysis.

Somatic manifestations also occur, of course, as part and parcel of an anxiety reaction. Freud noted certain characteristics about anxiety, particularly that it was accompanied by "fairly definite physical sensations which can be referred to particular organs of the body" (*13*, p. 97) and further that "motor innervations, i.e., processes of discharge, play a part in the general phenomenon of anxiety" (13, p. 97) and that anxiety differed from similar states like mourning and pain in that anxiety had motor manifestations; that there was (1) a specific quality of unpleasure, (2) acts of discharge, and (3) perceptions of those acts. And further, with the abandonment of the toxicological theory of anxiety and the formulation of the concept of anxiety as a danger signal, he indicated that each period of the individual's life has its appropriate determinant of anxiety. One might go a step further and speculate as to whether the somatic manifestations of anxiety might not also show a specificity of organic and motor discharge. Some aspects of this problem were presented by me some years ago (*19*).

A third form of somatic manifestation may be seen in what we now call psychosomatic illness. This may possibly be of two types: one, a specific physiopathological manifestation, perhaps not unlike the symbolically significant conversion symptom; and the other, a somatic manifestation which is purely secondary in nature as a direct result of a psychophysiological process that is reached and carried through as a result of a normal function that has become overdetermined and maintained over a long period of time, thus creating a climate in which the pathological phenomenon eventuates. Such a phenomenon may be the peptic ulcer resulting from an increase in hydrochloric acid in the gastric juice which in turn results from eating, or unconscious fantasies symbolically equivalent to eating. I am quite certain that Alexander's division between conversion symptoms and so-called vegetative neuroses will be discussed at great length.

There are other hypotheses which attempt to account for the individual systemic or somatic manifestations. One may accept that "Psychosomatic medicine is an operational approach to the theory and practice of medicine in which the structure and function of the psychic apparatus are dealt with as a variable in health and disease, just as, for example, are physiology and pathology. It is apparent that this definition requires that the psychological factor be homogenized into every aspect of the approach of a physician to a patient and into the pathogenetic conception of the disease process. It specifically denies the type of thinking in which the psychological factor is considered as a separate layer or as an afterthought in the evaluation of the patient" (25, pp. 609-610). With the emphasis on both health and disease, then, in principle many of our difficulties might be eliminated. The significant postulate for the purpose of what is to follow is that all psychic and somatic phenomena are in the broadest sense a resultant of the interplay between biological instinctual forces, ego forces, superego forces and reality demands. There is a constant adaptive homeostatic phenomenon which attempts to achieve an equilibrium, which may vary from moment to moment, in which one of the resultant variables may be a somatic symptom. In other words, placing the psychosomatic symptom within the framework of such an equilibrium will allow us the hypothetical possibility that a change in the relationship between the above systems or in the systems themselves may result in an equilibrium in which the psychosomatic symptom need not be one of the variables.

One might apply Waelder's principle of multiple function and his observations on overdetermination in this context in which there is a double or multiple concept of each psychic action. Since the functions of the ego are task solving, it always faces problems and seeks to find their solution. The ego then must contribute its part to any instinctual expression as it faces the id, the outside world, and the gradually developing superego. Since there is a compulsion to repeat, this presents a fourth problem for the ego. The ego is not only limited to a passive role but also has an active role in striving to hold its own and to assimilate "in organic growth the outer world as well as the other agencies within the individual" (31, p. 47). "There are then eight groups of problems whose solution is attempted by the ego: four of these are assigned to the ego and the other four the ego assigns to itself" (31, p. 48). Therefore, every attempted solution of a problem represents in some way or another an attempted solution of other problems. "Consequently, each psychic act can and must be conceived in every case as a simultaneous attempted solution of all eight problems, although it may be more successful as an attempted solution of one particular problem than of another" (31, p. 49). Since the organism always reacts in its entirety and since all problems are constantly living within it, each attempted solution must be "conjointly determined, modified and arranged through the existence and the working of the other, until it can serve, even if imperfectly, as an attempted solution for all these problems and thus necessarily preserve its multiple meaning" (*31*, p. 52).

He further makes the point that if one takes either one or a combination of more than one of the eight problems there may be from eight to many thousands of theories in regard to the genesis of neurosis. With these manifold hypothetical possibilities one can see how many theories of therapy might be evolved. If it is true that the change of one variable in the total picture changes the relationship of all other variables and that if any one of the dynamisms involved in total personality function can be utilized to change the total picture even though temporarily, then one can see how many therapeutic approaches, goal-limited to symptom disappearance, one may postulate.

In order to discuss therapeutic problems it is necessary to discuss therapeutic theories. This leads to a discussion of the evolution of the psychoanalytic therapy and its theoretical basis. If psychoanalysis is a definitive system of human psychology even though there are many unsolved problems, and if psychoanalytic therapy is the only therapy which can achieve basic and fundamental personality changes, it then follows that all changes that take place within the individual should be subject to explanation by psychoanalysis[2] and that the only definitive etiological therapy is psychoanalysis. Let us examine the theoretical basis of psychoanalytic ther-

[2] Some years ago I endeavored to examine factors in psychotherapy as understood by psychoanalysis. See (*18*).

apy in order to understand what factors are involved in this treatment process.

Throughout all the changes in technique and emphasis the main goal has always been what has been expressed in a number of what one might call slogans. "To make the unconscious conscious." "Where id was there shall ego be." "Psychoanalysis is an instrument to enable the ego to push its conquest of the id further still" (*12*, p. 82). In *Beyond the Pleasure Principle* the changes have been summarized in the following way: "Five-and-twenty years of intensive work have brought about a complete change in the more immediate aims of psychoanalytic technique. At first the endeavors of the analytic physician were confined to divining the unconscious of which his patient was unaware, effecting a synthesis of its various components and communicating it at the right time. Psychoanalysis was above all an art of interpretation. Since the therapeutic task was not thereby accomplished, the next aim was to compel the patient to confirm the reconstruction through his own memory. In this endeavor the chief emphasis was on the resistances of the patient; the art now lay in unveiling these as soon as possible, in calling the patient's attention to them, and by human influence—here came in suggestion acting as 'transference'—teaching him to abandon the resistances" (*11*, p. 17). It was followed by the statement that bringing into consciousness of the unconscious was not fully attainable and led to a discussion of the role of repetition compulsion. As early as 1910 Freud (*4*) noted the change in emphasis: first the early cathartic method whose aim was to elucidate the symptoms; then discovering of the complexes; and later the finding out and overcoming of resistances which would then allow the complexes to come to light. He drew attention to the phenomenon of countertransference and emphasized the biological function of the neuroses and stated that the therapeutic task lay in combating resistances. Transference phenomena were discussed and the relationship of repetition was emphasized. The patient ascribed currency and reality to what resulted from the awakening of his unconscious feelings, and he sought discharge of his emotions regardless of the reality of the situation. The physician required that the patient fit these emotions (a) into the treatment situation, (b) into the life history, (c) that he subject them to rational consideration, (d) that he appraise them at their true psychical value, and emphasized again the invaluable service of transference manifestations. These presented the greatest difficulty for the physician, but nevertheless rendered invaluable service in making the patient's repressed "love emotions actual and manifest. In the last resort no one can be slain *in absentia* or *in effigie*" (5, p. 322).

In 1912 he again returned to the transference problem and emphasized that the "loosening of the transference, too, one of the main tasks of the cure, is made more difficult by too intimate an attitude on the part of the doctor. A doubtful gain in the beginning is more than cancelled out in the end. Therefore, I do not hesitate to condemn this kind of technique as incorrect. The physician should be impenetrable to the patient and like a mirror reflecting nothing but what is shown him" (6, p. 331). In 1913 he set down certain rules for carrying on psychoanalysis—the principle of hire by the hour, five to six times a week. He discussed the wish for a shortening of the analytic treatment which he deemed as reasonable but stated that, "Unfortunately, it is opposed by a very important element in the situation, namely the slowness with which profound changes in the mind bring themselves about . . ." (7, p. 350). He made a further comment on what might happen when a patient was freed from one unendurable symptom, that he then might find that a previously negligible one had now increased until it became intolerable. Specifically, in relation to the problems of therapy in psychosomatic illness, Freud's injunction that if a patient required medical or special treatment it was wiser to call in some colleague outside of analytic work, has special relevance. Alexander in recent years has emphasized the need for such teamwork between the internist and psychiatrist. Of further relevance was the comment that "analysis combined with other treatment for neurotic maladies with a strong organic connection is nearly always impractical. The patient withdraws his interest from the analysis when there is more than one way leading to health" (7, p. 358). Freud has always emphasized that the primary motive power used in therapy was the patient's suffering and the wish to be cured. The fact that this alone was not sufficient was also stated. But of importance was the statement that "The transference alone frequently suffices to bring about a disappearance of the symptoms of the disease, but this is merely temporary and lasts only as long as the transference is maintained. The treatment is then nothing more than suggestion, not a psychoanalysis" (7, p. 365).

In 1914 discussing repetition, recollection and working through, there was an emphasis on the far-reaching changes in psychoanalytic technique since its beginning. In the early phases of catharsis there was a direct concentration upon the events exciting symptom formation with an intent to obtain reproduction of the mental processes involved in that situation in order to bring about a release of them through conscious operations. With the help of hypnosis the aims were "recollection" and "abreaction." Then the attempt was to overcome resistances by interpretation. Concentration on the situations giving rise to symptom formation and on those which lay behind the outbreak of illness were retained. There was less emphasis on abreaction with an attempt to overcome critical objections to free associations. Later, analysis abandoned concentration upon particular elements or problems and contented itself with studying whatever was in the patient's mind. It used interpretation primarily for recognizing resistances, and there was a rearrangement of the division of labor. The physician discovered resistances which were unknown to the patient. When these were removed, the patient often related forgotten situations and connections without any difficulty. "The aim of these different procedures has of course remained the same throughout. Descriptively, to recover the lost memories and dynamically, to conquer the resistances caused by repression" (8, p. 367). There was the emphasis on the fact that transference in itself was a bit of repetition and that this repetition of the forgotten past was not only in relation to the physician but in other aspects of the current situation. Since allowing repetition during analytic treatment constituted a conjuring into existence of a piece of

105

real life, it was not always harmless and the question of "exacerbation of symptoms during treatment" was linked up with this. In 1915 in a discussion of transference love it was pointed out that the forces with which the analyst worked were explosive and dangerous, but "I certainly do not advocate that the harmless methods of treatment should be abandoned. For many cases they suffice—but it is grossly to undervalue both the origins and the practical significance of the psychoneuroses to suppose that these disorders are to be removed by puttering about with a few harmless remedies. No, in medical practice there will always be room for the 'ferrum' and the 'ignis' as well as for the 'medicina,' and there a strictly regular unmodified psychoanalysis which is not afraid to handle the most dangerous forces in the mind and set them to work for the benefit of the patient will be found indispensable" (9, pp. 390-391).

A particularly important paper by Freud was the one on "Turnings in the Way of Psychoanalytic Therapy" in 1919, in which he made the statement that "It may be observed, incidentally, that unhappy marriage and bodily infirmity are the two things that most dissolve the neurosis . . . . a long organic illness they regard as punishment by fate and then often cease to keep up with their neurosis" (10, p. 397). This statement has particular importance in relation to the repeated observation in many clinics of the relationship between so-called psychosomatic illness and psychosis. That there is such a relationship there can be no doubt. Its meaning and significance is not too clear. Dr. Edward D. Joseph and I at our hospital are at the present time engaged in an attempt to gather pertinent clinical material in an effort to throw some light on this important phenomenon. A further statement by Freud is significant in relation to so-called need-fulfillment therapies in that he says, "Any analyst, who out of the fullness of his heart and his readiness to help perhaps extends to the patient all that one human being may hope to receive from another, commits the same economic error which our non-analytic institutions for nervous patients are guilty of. They exert themselves only to make everything as pleasant as possible for the patient, so that he may feel well there and gladly take flight back there again away from the trials of life. In so doing they entirely forego making him stronger for life and more capable of carrying out the actual tasks of his life. In analytic treatment all such cosseting must be avoided. As far as his relations with the physician are concerned, the patient must have unfulfilled wishes in abundance. It is expedient to deny him precisely those satisfactions which he desires most intensely and expresses most importunately" (*10*, p. 398). And it is also in this paper that Freud made the statement that is perhaps most widely quoted in relation to any discussion of psychoanalytically based nonpsychoanalytic therapy. "The task will then arise for us to adapt our technique to the new conditions. I have no doubt that the validity of our psychological assumptions will impress the uneducated too, but we shall need to find the simplest and most natural expression for our theoretical doctrines. We shall probably discover that the poor are even less ready to part with their neuroses than the rich, because the hard life that awaits them when they recover has no attraction, and illness in them gives them more claim to the help of others. Possibly we may often only be able to achieve something if we combine aid for the mind with some material support, in the manner of Emperor Joseph. It is very probable, too, that the application of our therapy to numbers will compel us to alloy the pure gold of analysis plentifully with the copper of direct suggestion; and even hypnotic influence might find a place in it again, as it has in the treatment of war-neuroses.[3] But whatever form this psychotherapy for the people may take, whatever the elements out of which it is compounded, its most effective and most important ingredients will assuredly remain those borrowed from strict psychoanalysis which serves no ulterior purpose" (10, pp. 401-402).

I should like further to elaborate a point that I touched upon previously, and that is that psychoanalysis has an obligation to explain the symptom loss that ostensibly results from many varied therapeutic attempts. In other words, the miracles—Lourdes, Christian Science, Chiropractic, placebos, psychobiological analysis and synthesis, psychoanalysis, anaclitic therapy, sector therapy and many others—need a theoretical explanation based on psychoanalytic psychology. Most of us know, for instance, that Maurice Levine has listed under methods and elements of psychotherapy twenty-five methods for the nonpsychiatrist for use in "suitable cases," five advanced methods for the nonpsychiatrist "(who has some added training and aptitude) for use in suitable cases," and eight methods for the psychiatrist. All of these methods "in suitable cases" will result in a symptom loss (21, pp. 17-19).

[3] For use of hypnosis in World War II see (20).

There are many papers on the problems of therapy in psychoanalysis, and I have selected some of them for the purposes of this discussion. Some of the most significant contributions in this area have been made by Nunberg in a series of papers which are now collected in the book on *Practice and Theory of Psychoanalysis*. In the paper on "Problems of Therapy" Nunberg emphasized that the neurosis develops from a rift between the strivings of the id and the demands of the ego and that the therapeutic task is principally that of making peace between the two parts of the personality—the ego and the id—so that the instincts no longer lead a separate existence outside of the ego organization and that since the synthetic function of the ego is disturbed in neurosis, the therapy aims also at the recovery by the ego of its synthetic power. Therefore, "To influence the ego as well as the id becomes the goal of the therapeutic task" (27, p. 108). Nunberg elaborates on a point which is of the utmost significance. He reiterated that "every suffering and sick human being is helpless, and in his helplessness like a child he over-estimates the power of anyone who promises help" (27, p. 108). The patient looks upon the physician as a magician since the physician will protect him by magical means from the dangers presented by the instincts. In another paper on "Psychological Interrelations between Physician and Patient," he elaborates this and points out that the patient believes in the physician without reserve in the same way that he once believed in his parents. In his superstitious way he expects the physician to perform miracles for him as his parents did. Through identification with the father, the boy not only overcomes his fear

109

of the father and not only acquires power over his mother, but also becomes omniscient and omnipotent, and therefore in later life if such an individual becomes a physician and "still has not lost his magic omnipotence through adaptation to reality, he will be disturbed in his professional efficiency. He will think he is really omnipotent and undertake certain measures that are beyond his powers and capability" (27, p. 181). Since in reality the physician is really powerful through his knowledge, it may become relatively easy for the patient to shift the omnipotence from his parents to the physician. It was a great temptation for the physician to accept this role. "Sickness is magic and healing is counter-magic" (27, p. 182).[4] When the physician makes conscious use of the "patient's magic superstitions, we call it in modern times suggestive therapy" (27, p. 182). The physician as a magician represents unconsciously not only the father but the mother, and the first care by mother is sensed by the infant as magic.

In another paper on "The Synthetic Function of the Ego" Nunberg develops a theme which is of great importance in relation to our problem. With the development of the superego, the ego's task becomes more complicated. It reconciles the conflicting elements within the id, allies them with one another so that there is unanimity of feeling, action and will, since the ego tolerates no contradiction. Secondly, it brings the instinctual trends of the id into harmony with the requirements of reality; and third, it strikes a balance between the claims of the superego on one hand and of reality

[4] See also Castiglioni (2) and Sigerist (28).

on the other. The synthetic function of the ego manifests itself in assimilating alien elements both from within and without and mediates between opposing elements, even reconciling opposites, setting mental productivity in motion. There is a need for causality which Nunberg relates to the synthetic tendency of Eros in a sublimated form in the ego and that this represents a very important principle—that of connection in the psychic realm as a whole. He comments on other psychotherapeutic methods in this way: "It is probable that other psychotherapeutic methods, including those which call themselves psychoanalytic without being so, attack the illness from this point also. But the essential difference between all these methods and our own is that in the former, patients have to assimilate something forced upon them from without, whereas in psychoanalysis by a process of painful self-mastery they have to admit into their ego and unite with it that which is a fundamental part of their own nature. This is probably one reason why many patients may be cured even though their analysis is not fully completed, provided that they accept and acknowledge as their own, repressed material whose existence it has been possible to infer in their analysis, although it has not actually been remembered" (27, p. 136).

This synthetic function of the ego and the need for causality plays an extraordinarily important role in all modalities of therapy, as has already been indicated by Nunberg. Many patients utilize this in rationalization, and the acceptance or the creation of an interpretation or perspective which may or may not have any reality validity is a sort of "peg to hang their hat on" and fulfills the need for a different kind of equilibrium which does not involve symptom formation. This is also part of the need for completion or the formation of a gestalt. Their role in symptom loss should not be underestimated.

There have been a number of symposia on problems of therapy. In 1948 there was a symposium on "The Evaluation of Therapeutic Results" (29) held in this place in which Oberndorf, Greenacre and Kubie participated. Some of the comments made at that time are relevant. For instance, Greenacre cited the fact that Freud sensed the danger of too great therapeutic zeal in the analyst. She made certain proposals regarding the problem of evaluation, and I will requote part of her quotation from Freud. " *'It is better to examine one's own individual experience.* As to that I may say that I do not think our successes can compete with those of Lourdes.'" (29, p. 8). Kubie, in his own inimitable fashion and with the thoroughness for which he is justly famous, set down a list of fourteen points which would be essential for an adequate survey of the therapeutic processes which covered every aspect of the problem. I quote these in order to emphasize the complexity of the problems involved (29, pp. 13-14).

"G. THE FOLLOWING LIST SUMMARIZES MOST OF THE DATA WHICH SEEMS TO BE ESSENTIAL FOR AN ADEQUATE SURVEY OF THE THERAPEUTIC PROCESS:

"(1) An outline of the symptoms and difficulties which brought the patient for treatment and their duration prior to treatment.

"(2) An estimate of what the normal outcome of such a condition would be, if untreated.

"(3) The initial over-all 'diagnosis' and the evidence for this diagnosis.

"(4) The general state of the patient's life adjustment at the onset of the treatment (i.e., the extent to which the neurosis had already crippled the patient's life).

"(5) The general social situation of the patient at the onset of the treatment (economic, familial, marital, professional, etc.); and important changes in life situations occurring during treatment.

"(6) The conditions under which the treatment was undertaken (as to financial arrangements, time arrangements, travel arrangements, holidays, etc.); and the extent to which these conditions were adhered to and remained constant throughout the treatment, or were changed, either deliberately or of necessity.

"(7) Special difficulties against which the treatment had to labour, arising from forces beyond the control of the therapist; such as outside interferences, physical illness, unavoidable interruptions, opposition by other members of the family, the attitude of other medical advisers, and especially the family physician.

"(8) Specially advantageous circumstances which favorably affected the course and outcome of the treatment: especially the stability or instability of attitudes of family, friends, and family physician, and also the absence of all factors under number 7 above.

"(9) The duration and continuity of the treatment; and influence of accidental and/or intentional interruptions (i.e., purposeful or unintended).

"(10) The general course of the treatment; critical disturbances during its course (symptomatic or in behaviour).

"(1) The disclosure of masked symptoms during the course of treatment; any modification in the diagnostic and prognostic interpretation of the case as a result of this.

"(12) The therapeutic outcome as estimated by (a) the final symptomatic state; (b) the final state of the patient's general life adjustment as contrasted with this at the beginning.

"(13) The final diagnosis as based upon the additional material uncovered in the treatment and its resolution.

"(14) Follow-up data."

Bandler cited a case which certainly emphasized the need for a thorough knowledge of all the factors involved before one was in the position to state with any degree of definiteness as to what the factors in any therapeutic result actually were (29, p. 19). I refer to the case involving the resident and the vaginal dilator.

In a symposium on "The Theory of the Therapeutic Results of Psychoanalysis" (30) held in Marienbad, Glover, Fenichel, Strachey, Bergler, Nunberg and Bibring participated. There is a marked contrast in emphasis by the participants in regard to what the principal factors in psychoanalytic therapy are. Fenichel stated, "The old formula 'we cure by making the unconscious conscious' is *topographically* conceived, and there is a danger that in our technique we may do too scant justice to the *dynamic* and *economic* standpoints. In my view it is not simply the function of reality-testing that depends on the superego: *all* the ego-functions are accessible to the superego's influence" (30, p. 138). Strachey emphasized the need to help the patient develop "toward the genetic level at which his whole tendency to internal conflict will be automatically diminished. An improvement of this kind will from its very nature be permanent, and it is at an improvement of this kind that psychoanalysis aims" (*30*, p. 140). He emphasized that the analyst's endeavor from the very beginning was "to differentiate himself from the patient's archaic objects and to contrive, as far as he possibly can, that the patient shall introject him not as one more archaic imago added to the rest of the primitive superego but as the nucleus of a separate and new superego" (*30*, p. 144). His main conclusions were that the immediate determinants of the therapeutic results in analysis were in the procedures of interpretation, particularly transference interpretation, and to understand how these procedures operated it was necessary to pay attention to the mechanism of introjection and projection.

E. Bibring presented one of the most penetrating discussions of the problem. He emphasized the need for relating a theory of therapeutic procedure with a theory of therapeutic results. He made the point that spontaneous cures may occur and stated that psychoanalytic therapy aimed at various things. "Broadly speaking, where id was ego shall be. . . . The aim of therapy may therefore be provisionally described as a change in the reciprocal relations between the various institutions of the mind. This alteration includes a change *within* these institutions, i.e., within the id, the superego, and most especially and decisively, within the ego. . . . The *means* employed are, in the first instance, making the unconscious conscious: and by unconscious is here meant not

115

only the id but also the unconscious parts of the ego (the superego and the unconscious methods of modification, i.e., the ego-mechanisms)" (*30*, pp. 170-171). He proceeds to a very interesting and profitable discussion involving these relations on a structural basis and has a great deal which is pertinent and relevant to our discussion which unfortunately lack of time does not permit me to go into.

Any discussion of therapy that involves psychoanalysis must include Freud's classical paper on "Analysis Terminable and Interminable" which is a distillation of Freud's total experience with psychoanalysis as a therapy. Discussing the technique of setting a termination date, he makes the point that "the analysis was in danger of failing as a result of its partial success" (*14*, p. 374). This is of significance since a new equilibrium which contains some neurotic compromises may, because of partial success, lead to stagnation. From our point of view, however, it is the fact that a partial success resulting in loss of symptoms is possible. Rather than talking about the end of an analysis in certain cases, it might be better to deem such analyses as incomplete. Only if the analysis were to result in no further change if continued, if all repressions were lifted, if all the memory gaps were filled, and accepting the implication that analysis made it possible to attain "absolute psychic normality" which is maintained might one speak of completion. In some cases there has been a success in clearing up the patient's neurosis without any relapses or other neurotic manifestations following. In those instances no noticable change takes place in the patient's ego, and Freud infers that this type of ill-

116

ness is preëminently traumatic. He emphasized that the etiology of all neuroses is a mixed one where either the patient's instincts are excessively strong and do not submit to the restraining influence of the ego or the patient suffers "from the affects of premature traumas by which I mean traumas which his immature ego was unable to surmount." When traumatic factors predominate, one can attain "that most masterly achievement of psychoanalysis, namely such a reinforcement of the ego that a correct adjustment takes the place of that infantile solution of the patient's early conflicts which proved so inadequate" (*14*, p. 377), and only then can one speak about a definitive end to an analysis.

The constitutional strength of instinct and the unfavorable change of the ego in the defensive conflict are prejudicial to analysis. Freud's own attitude toward the question of how analysis works therapeutically is shown in the following quotation. "Instead of inquiring how analysis affects a cure (a point which in my opinion has been sufficiently elucidated), we should ask what are the obstacles which this cure encounters" (*14*, p. 377). The constitutional factor has always been considered of importance, *but it is yet conceivable that the same effects might ensue from a reinforcement of instinctual energy at some later period of life.*" Since such a reinforcement is possible, the obverse is also possible and a weakening or change in energic forces may lead to a diminution in the conflict situation so that one would have to say with Freud "the strength of the instincts at a given moment" (*14*, p. 381) is the important factor.

In regard to the ego in its conflict with instinctual demands, he emphasized that it was the particular re-

117

lationship maintained between the strength of the instinct and that of the ego which was important, that any enfeeblement of the ego through illness, exhaustion or other causes may result in a renewal of the instinctual strivings "in abnormal ways after substitutive gratification," and he related this to "a justification of the etiological pretensions of such indefinite factors as overwork, shock, etc." (*14*, p. 382). The function of analysis was to enable the mature ego to review old repressions so that some are lifted and others accepted after reconstruction "from more solid material. . . . Thus, the real achievement of analytic therapy is a subsequent correction of the original process of repression, with the result that a supremacy of the quantitative factor is brought to an end" (*14*, p. 383). In relation to partial results, he stated that it might "be parts of the old mechanisms remained untouched by analysis. . . . We have to be careful not to imagine that the clarity of our own insight is a measure of the conviction we produce in the mind of the analysand" (*14*, p. 385). He questions whether a latent conflict can be transformed into a present one, in either one of two ways. Either by creating a situation in which the conflict becomes actual, that is, either in reality or in the transference, or one can content oneself with discussing the possibility of such a conflict arising. The patient in either case is exposed to real suffering "through frustration and the damming up of libido" (*14*, p. 386). Since analysis progresses best when "the patient's pathogenic experiences belong to the past so that the ego can stand at a distance from them" (*14*, p. 387), the use of analysis in acute crises is almost impossible, since the whole interest of the ego is concentrated on the painful reality. He warns against deliberate procedures which would necessitate "unkind behavior" by the therapist since it would have a deleterious effect on the positive transference which is the strongest motive for coöperation. "So we shall not form any high expectation of the results of such a technique" (*14*, p. 388).

Traumatic factors, relative strength of the instincts and modification of the ego relate to the success of therapy. The analyst, in alliance with part of the ego of the analysand, attempts to subdue certain parts of the id which have not been mastered; in other words, to include them in the synthesis of the ego. Defensive techniques may in themselves become dangerous. They produce an ever-growing alienation from the outside world and a permanent enfeeblement of the ego. In treatment they become resistances to the cure. The outcome of an analysis depends "principally upon the strength and depth of the roots of the resistances constituting the ego modification" (*14*, p. 394).

The importance of primal, congenital ego variations which is decisive for the choice of only certain defense mechanisms is stressed. This is related to the constitutional endowment of the individual ego. There is a discussion of "resistances from the id" which is reformulated as a situation in which all the mental processes, relations and distributions of energy are immutable, fixed and rigid. The role of behavior of the two primal instincts, their distribution, fusion and defusion which cannot be confined to "a single province of the mental apparatus whether it be id, ego or superego. . . . Only by the interaction and counteraction of the two primal

instincts—Eros and the death instinct—never by one or
the other alone, can the motley variety of vital phenomena be explained" (*14*, pp. 396-397).

The basic clash between heterosexuality and homo-
sexuality or the reverse is discussed. The importance of
the role of free aggression in the spontaneous tendency
to conflict is emphasized. One point which Freud makes
is of particular importance in regard to the function of
therapies that are utilized in a general hospital, namely,
"finally we must not forget that the relationship between analyst and patient rests on the love of truth as
its foundations, that is, on the acknowledgment of reality, and it precludes every sort of sham and deception"
(*14*, p. 401).

In this paper he also discusses the qualifications
necessary for a psychoanalyst. Many of these qualifications are pertinent for anyone who wishes to do psychotherapy, and finally he comes to what he calls the bed-
rock of the task, that is, the penis wish in the woman
and the masculine protest in the man, "for in the psychic field the biological factor is really the rock-bottom"
(*14*, p. 405), and he concludes his paper with the following words: "Whether and when we have succeeded
in mastering this factor in an analysis is hard to determine. We console ourselves with the certainty that
everything possible has been done to rouse the analysand to examine and to change his attitude in this respect" (*14*, p. 405).

There are many reasons for summarizing this paper
by Freud that are particularly relevant to the topic of
our discussion today, since actually most of the therapeutic approaches to the problem of psychosomatic ill-

ness are goal-limited, and it is of some importance to indicate the limitations inherent in even the most thoroughgoing psychoanalysis.

To return to a discussion of different therapies which are based on a psychoanalytic orientation, these may all result in the disappearance of the somatic and other symptoms and yet are basically and theoretically at great variance with each other. I have selected five of these techniques for brief presentation.[5] Four of these were presented at the recent round table on "Psychotherapy in Medical and Surgical Hospitals" (15) by Grinker, Ludwig, Engel and Margolin, and the fifth is the goal-limited Sector Therapy of Felix Deutsch.

George L. Engel in a paper entitled "The Surrogate Ego Role of the Physician in the Management of the Physically Sick Patients" (3) bases his observations on what he calls a unitary concept of health and disease in which he attempts to take into account and relate different types of phenomena observed in the sick person. There are two basic premises: (1) that health and disease are defined as "phases of life dependent at any time on the balance maintained by devices, genetically and experimentally determined, intent on fulfilling needs and on adapting to and mastering stresses as they "may arise from within the organism or from without"; (2) that the needs of the organism have a biologically determined source in instinctual energy, but that the satisfaction of these needs is accomplished by biological, psychological and social devices, mainly aiming at the maintenance of a stable dynamic equilibrium between

[5] There are, of course, many others; i.e., the work of the Chicago Institute of Psychoanalysis as reported extensively.

121

the internal and external environments. One can immediately see that this formulation is essentially similar to the one I have presented above. The clinical picture of illness in symptoms and signs stems from four components: (1) attempts at satisfaction of instinctual needs that have been interfered with, which may be simultaneously represented at biological, psychological and social levels as well as different developmental levels; (2) an inner perception of a disturbance in equilibrium which is interpreted as a danger and reacted to with anxiety, setting in motion adaptive devices; (3) the adaptive devices themselves at all levels; and (4) the actual structural and functional changes which result from the stress. He also points out that each manifestation may be overdetermined.

This paper discusses specifically many of the problems that relate to the patient in a hospital which make the therapeutic regime necessarily different from that used with the ambulatory patient. The differences occur in the relationship to family and the relationship to the physician in the hospital. The main thesis is that "To varying degrees, the physician functions as a surrogate ego during the patient's illness. This is a consequence of the interference by the physical process with the perceptive, executive and integrative aspects of ego function. . ." (3). This is regarded as analagous to a childhood situation when the child's ego functions were limited and "when mother and other adult figures functioned for the child's ego, especially in interpreting and dealing with external reality." Clinical material is presented in order to exemplify the various problems involved with the conclusion that if the psychological problems are understood, the therapist may then function rationally in the indicated role, and in this role the physician uses "whatever devices and carries out whatever manipulations that fit in with the current ego position of the patient and conserves the patient's energy resources for the immediate task at hand." The understanding of the actual transference situation is important in order to enable the physician "successfully to fill this role." At times deliberate efforts are to be made in order to help "the patient identify the physician with a helpful rather than a threatening figure in his past life." As a result of these manipulations various things may happen including the disappearance of the somatic symptom.

Grinker (15) in his paper on "Psychotherapy in Medical and Surgical Hospitals" points out the role of the psychoanalytic psychiatrist in the problems of the acutely ill patient. Since psychoanalysis is not possible and it is sometimes questionable as to how much psychotherapy can be done in the hospital in view of the busyness of the scene, the task may have to be limited to "adequate diagnosis, understanding of the multiple interacting factors of patient, environment and doctors as they have been genetically related to the causes of the illness and as they relate in the present to the hastening or impedance of recovery." Thus one might prevent harm to the patient and encourage promising directions of recovery. Forces that are brought into play by the physician may have an impact on the relatives, nurses and "hospital ritualists"; relationships with the patient may satisfy his needs of the moment and "facilitate his participation in the recovery processes." Then he states, "But when it comes to direct psychotherapeutic intervention the patient must be handled alone by the psychiatrist without interference, in privacy and with plenty of time." Thus Grinker recognizes that with the understanding of the patient and his problems many things may be done directly and with the milieu which may result in amelioration of the conditions or even the disappearance of the somatic symptoms; but he emphasizes the need for an intimate, private relationship for fundamental psychotherapy.

For some years now at The Mount Sinai Hospital a therapeutic approach which has been based on Freud's original concept of the anaclitic relationship has been the framework for our treatment endeavors with our patients. The organization of our ward service is such that the Psychiatrist-in-Charge who is one of the senior members[6] of the staff rotates yearly. During this period he has complete responsibility and authority for the clinical management of the ward. This has resulted in variations of this technique in line with the understanding and, to some extent, the personality of the Psychiatrist-in-Charge. In Child Psychiatry, under the immediate supervision of Dr. Abram Blau, a similar approach has been practiced in the care of the patients assigned to our service or for the patients for whom the liaison psychiatrist shares treatment responsibility under the direction of the Pediatrician to the hospital. Since September 1951 Dr. Sydney G. Margolin has been the Psychiatrist-in-Charge of the psychiatry ward. He

[6] Dr. Abram Blau, Dr. Paul Goolker, Dr. Sydney G. Margolin, Dr. Harry I. Weinstock, and Dr. S. Mouchly Small (now at University of Buffalo).

has been carrying out an organized investigation of the factors that enter into this type of treatment situation. A preliminary report of the findings was presented at the above panel under the title of "Anaclitic Therapy in Organic Disease" (23). Summarized, his specific modification, as reported, can be described as follows.

The total therapeutic approach is hypothetically related to the organization of the hospital and specifically the Psychiatry Service. The factor of selectivity in relation to the type of patient that we are likely to get; the actual teaching program, which is essentially for the training of the residents; the personnel available to the service, i.e., attending psychiatrist, resident, nurses, caseworker, psychologists, occupational therapists— these are all integrated into the final pattern. Margolin, as he has stated, has divided the treatment arbitrarily into three phases, each phase having "a nodal point at which a change in the therapeutic aim occurs." The first phase exploits the patient's unconscious tendency to revert to "a level of regression which reënacts the infantile conflict that is genetically and characterologically related to his disease." This becames apparent in the compulsive transference reaction and also allows for a dependency attitude which "favors external help." Under these circumstances the therapist "assumes a role of total permissiveness and does not thwart the regression." An attempt is made to forego all formalistic routine aspects of the hospital even to the extent of doing away with scheduled interviews so that the therapist is available at any time. Margolin makes the analogue of a "'demand-feeding' schedule." This permissive tolerant attitude extends to all personnel of the ward. All physical needs are "anticipated and indulged" even to the extent of the therapist preparing and providing food. The postprandial relationship "between the patients and the doctors is of the greatest importance." The degree of relaxation, drowsiness and wish to rest and to sleep on the part of the patient are related to the efficacy of the therapy. To further the regression to an infantile psychophysiological equilibrium the patient may be "touched and handled, and areas of pain and discomfort are massaged and stroked. The therapist is actively comforting and reassuring with an attitude of omniscience and omnipotence." After some time the dependency situation is marked. His behavior usually is highly ambivalent, and the nodal point is the appearance of "a fixed and highly focused dependency." There is no interpretation to this point of the unconscious meaning of the behavior, and "the therapist becomes part of the perceptual and executive apparatus of the patient's ego by both anticipating and gratifying his needs without discussion with the patient." This is of interest in view of Engel's premise (3). The behavior of the therapist at the later part of this stage could be called "preverbal interpretations." Dealing with the patient at the level of symbolic gratification only "can be regarded as thwarting the patient's instinctual expression and stressing his ego boundaries" (23). The patient's wishes are gratified at a symbolic and not overt instinctual level.

There is a discussion of the effect on the therapist which perhaps Margolin may further elaborate during this symposium. The resident, as therapist, works under supervision of the attending psychiatrist who takes the report of the therapist's experience with the patient together with the details of the associated conditions and circumstances and structures them as if they were the manifest content of a dream and then "this 'dream' is interpreted in order to disclose both the patient's instinctual wishes and the therapist's countertransference." The correctness of the interpretation "is estimated by three circumstances: (1) an increase in regression; (2) an alteration in the patient's mood; and (3) what is most important evidence of physiological regression." Margolin, himself, raises the point as to the validity of psychoanalytic interpretations in these circumstances. This is a point to which I will return, since in all three of the papers cited, this is a basic premise in the total evaluation of the situation and the procedures that follow.

The second phase of the anaclitic therapy has the goal of treating "this induced 'neurosis' and of restoring to the patient some of the ego functions which were given up in the psychotherapeutic relationship." The third phase is that of character analysis with its emphasis on ego psychology. The second phase attempts to stabilize and advance the physiological remission and also to initiate favorable characterological changes. It is emphasized that the second and third phases cannot be carried out during the relatively short stay in the hospital but must be followed by further therapy either in our own follow-up clinic or through psychoanalysis.

There is an emphasis on the assumption that the "goal is a physiological remission which never occurs without a mood change" and that "the association of affective mood changes with the remissions and relapses in these diseases is the single striking finding around which the therapy is mobilized" (23). If one follows this latter statement to its logical significance as Margolin, himself, does in a discussion of ACTH and Cortisone effects (24), then one must infer that any therapeutic approach, chemical or psychotherapeutic, which results in a mood change will lead to a physiological remission or exacerbation. Therefore, one may ask whether the preliminary therapy as outlined is intrinsically a necessary part of a total therapeutic approach or whether other techniques may not be as effective as long as they lead to a change in mood.

From our point of view perhaps the most significant paper presented at the panel was Ludwig's (22), in which there was a report of psychoanalytic observations with a group of patients with rheumatoid arthritis. Certain psychodynamic and economic formulations in regard to the factors playing a role in the possible etiology and course of this syndrome are reported. It is demonstrated that there is a relationship between specific dynamic changes and remissions of symptoms. A tentative formulation of the important factors is proposed. The close relationship between psychosis and rheumatoid arthritis is reported, and the emphasis on the "symbiotic" relationship between the patient and the mother is emphasized. The role of separation from any object as a trauma is indicated together with the poor tolerance for any frustrating experience especially relating to object loss and the mobilization of primary destructive drives with the specific defense reaction is discussed. Ludwig feels that the somatic symptoms of arthritis "like the overt manifestations of a psychosis, appears to operate as a restitutional mechanism" and states that "psychotherapy in this disorder must take cognizance of a number of facts: (1) affect is largely or even solely expressed through autonomic and somatic channels, with blocking of outward expression; (2) the ego is very weak, precariously situated, and fragmented, crushed between overpowering primitive id forces, and a punitive archaic superego; (3) frustration and exposure to renewed trauma leads to violent internal reactions and renewed exacerbations; (4) the disease itself leads eventually to irreversible joint damage and physical disability, varying in severity to complete invalidism; (5) the physical disability furnishes marked and welcome secondary gain in gratifying passive dependent needs. The psychotherapeutic methods and goals must vary with the stage of the disease . . ." (22).

There is also a discussion of the countertransference attitudes in the therapist and the role that these play in the total therapeutic situation. The relationship to the so-called anaclitic therapy is indicated by the statement that "This can be accomplished by any means so long as the fundamental need of the patient is fulfilled, and greater or less support will be necessary from the physician depending on the availability of other sources of support to the patient." The ultimate goal of therapy is to " 'separate' the patient from his symbiotic relationship." There is a utilization of psychoanalysis with certain modifications in relation to the position of the patient, the use of the couch and other modifications that are based on the particular dangers and defensive techniques the patient shows. It is of interest that patients' symptoms have disappeared after the overt expression of anger. The fear of being controlled or controlling others magically by incorporation and destruction is seen. The author feels that there is a definite demonstrable relationship between the "emotional meaning and reaction to events and the exacerbations of the joint symptoms, and that the course of the disease can be influenced by psychotherapeutic methods" (22).

His final statement is of especial interest, especially to us at The Mount Sinai Hospital in the light of our work with gastrointestinal fistulae (26, 16), since he states that he plans "eventually to define the unconscious meaning for these patients of the usual medical therapeutic methods employed in this disease" and that the final aim "is to gain sufficient understanding of the unconscious factors at play so that psychiatrist, internist and general practitioner may be furnished with psychotherapeutic methods for dealing with this disease, which are feasible for the degree of his psychiatric understanding and training and which can be utilized in the circumstance of his practice" (22). This last statement fits in directly with my own emphasis in this paper: that therapeutic techniques at various levels may result in symptom loss.

In regard to Deutsch's technique of Sector Psychotherapy (1), I shall make only a brief statement since he is present here and will undoubtedly present his formulations *in extenso*. His technique is essentially one of verbalization which aims at "the dissolution of these chains (association chains), and the replacement by new ones is in fact the therapeutic process. The extensive use of symbolic language may reveal sometimes an unexplained therapeutic success. Under the cover of the disguised words the patient has made indirect confessions, has expressed fears and guilt feelings and has eased up tensions" (1, p. 26). The associative anamnesis method in itself is an indirect psychotherapy, since it links up "as soon as possible a manifest symptom or problem of the present with the underlying conflicts and their expression in the past. The free associations guide the patient into the past but the technique confronts him continually with reality" (1, p. 23). Sector psychotherapy aims at the destruction of the "former unit of a memory, the nucleus of which remains unchanged. The therapeutic procedure consists in using contents of a memory as links for new forceful associations which are sufficiently powerful to loosen these links from their former connections" (1, p. 28).

Thus Deutsch's technique is essentially one of verbalization. Superficial psychotherapy, or the anaclitic technique as formulated by Margolin, is in its first phase essentially a nonverbal technique. The therapist is placed in a certain role in which he anticipates and fulfills the needs of the patient. There are mood changes reported upon which great emphasis is placed. In many instances this may lead to a "physiological remission." Grinker emphasizes knowledge and conservatism and the need for prolonged individual, time-consuming therapy in privacy. Engel's therapy in many ways resembles that which is done at The Mount Sinai Hospital. His therapeutic emphasis, however, is on the surrogate ego role of the physician.

I have rather carefully refrained up to this point from discussing specific clinical therapeutic problems. However, I cannot conclude this paper without presenting some clinical illustrations of the type of problem that is met with in a general hospital.

A male patient was admitted to the service as an emergency, bleeding from the rectum, with an authenticated diagnosis of ulcerative colitis. There was a history of periodic bouts of ulcerative colitis for about twelve years. Some four years before admission, he began intensive psychotherapy. Within *twelve* sessions his physical symptoms disappeared and remained in abeyance for the following four years. Several weeks before admission, apparently related to a constellation of circumstances, a recurrence of his ulcerative colitis took place. He was hemorrhaging profusely from the bowel and had to be admitted to a general hospital. His somatic symptoms cleared up fairly rapidly, to be followed by another recurrence with massive hemorrhage.

The patient had a good deal of "insight" into various unconscious factors which seemed to be related to his illness and somewhat continually ruminated about these. Since his physical condition was steadily going down-hill, and since the surgeon's opinion at that time was that he was too ill for operative procedure, a drastic psychotherapeutic step was undertaken which consisted essentially in his being told emphatically and dramatically that he would die from his hemorrhage unless he got hold of himself. Within twelve hours his hemorrhage ceased.

A somewhat similar situation with equally dramatic results occurred in relation to a seventeen-year-old boy with ulcerative colitis whose clinical picture changed in a specific fashion after the direct confrontation with the dangerous position that he was in because of the diffuse hemorrhage.

There are, of course, many possibilities inherent in both of these situations, not the least of which is coincidence. Nevertheless, temporally, the remission followed confrontation. This technique is not advocated as a treatment for patients hemorrhaging from ulcerative colitis but is intended to point up some of the factors discussed above.

We have had five, as yet unpublished, cases in status asthmaticus who did not respond to the usual medical procedures—adrenalin, aminophyllin, oxygen, etc.—in whom in each instance the status was terminated by hypnosis with a return to normal breathing as soon as the patients could accept the suggestions that they would breathe slowly and rhythmically and that they would fall asleep and reawaken minus their asthmatic attack.

One patient with neurodermatitis who has been reported (17) lost her skin manifestations dramatically during the course of the week following hypnosis. This patient developed an overt psychosis for which she was subsequently hospitalized in a state hospital and given shock therapy with recovery. A follow-up showed her to be in a remission from both her neurodermatitis and her psychosis four years later.

There is a need for complete coöperation between different departments in a general hospital for the treatment of the patient. The closest coöperation between the internist, the surgeon, and the various specialties and the psychiatrist is essential. We must remember that patients in a general hospital require not only psychotherapy but other medical procedures as indicated, whether these be dietary, pharmacological or other adjuvants. The psychiatrist who forgets this loses his practical function. It should always be realized that we are dealing with sick people in hospital practice in whom there may be a high morbidity and even mortality rate. Ulcerative colitis, asthma and other such illnesses kill people.

There are many problems in ward management which tax the ingenuity and countertransference of all personnel. There are many administrative problems. Above all, there are the relatives whom Freud about gave up, but with whom we have to deal. The psychiatrist in a general hospital is the physician who should be most capable of tolerating reality frustration. It is essential for the psychiatrist to have flexibility without compromising his function.

The importance of the above papers to my own thesis in regard to psychotherapy in psychosomatic disease cannot be overstressed. Although there is some obvious overlapping, there is also considerable divergence. Nevertheless, patients lose symptoms. Another aspect of these treatment programs is that they require a great deal of interpretation of what is going on. This interpretation can only be based on a minimum of individual specificity and a maximum of generality, and this perhaps is the most valid criticism that can be applied since, without "the omnipotence and omniscience" that Margolin has referred to, this really is scientifically an impossible task. Therefore, remembering Nunberg's formulation in regard to the magician role of the little boy grown-to-physician, it becomes essential that we do not overestimate our own capabilities and to remember that things do not necessarily always happen in the way we fantasied, no matter how logically we have presented our system to ourselves. This in no way attempts to underestimate the important contribution which the psychoanalyst can make, because he is a psychoanalyst, to his own understanding of the factors involved. However, in many instances what has happened has been merely a change in the relationships between the soma, id, ego, superego and reality. Many of the factors which I have enumerated above have come into play, and therefore a resultant change in equilibrium has occurred in which the psychosomatic symptom is no longer a necessary part.

This review of some basic postulates in the gradual evolution of psychoanalytic therapy was presented for various reasons. It was my intention to demonstrate that in the various forms of goal-limited therapies utilized at the present time, each one of the stages in the development of psychoanalytic therapy have played a part. Indeed, each one of these stages is still employed as a form of therapy.

The additional point that I wish to make is a rather simple and perhaps naive one in the present state of our theoretical knowledge. I have tried to emphasize that the psychosomatic symptoms have their own complex dynamic, genetic, topographic, economic and structural history like other symptoms. They serve, in principle, as one of the variable end results or results on the way toward an end in the establishment of an exceedingly complicated adaptive process in an homeostatic equilibrium. There may be many different forms of psychotherapy utilizing different mechanisms which make for a change in the quantitative factors in the id, in a positive or a negative direction; for changes in the ego, as for example through identification, supportive or other means; in the superego through identification, tolerance, or even increased severity, or other means; and in the reality situation of the individual. In other words, any change which leads to a new alignment of intersystemic forces or intrasystemic forces may lead to a situation in which the psychosomatic symptom no longer is an essential part of this new equilibrium. Therefore, it would seem to me that hypothetically psychoanalysis, with whatever flexibility may be necessary in the individual case, would be the only definitive, etiological treatment in psychosomatic illness. Beyond this we have at this time no definitive therapy; all therapies that have been described, in one way or another, are therapies aimed at symptoms rather than etiology. We must not allow our unconscious omnipotence and omniscience to interfere with our objectivity. We must realize that the therapeutic changes which are obtained are not always necessarily the result of what we think we do, but are rather the result of forces, the nature of which we have not as yet completely understood.

BIBLIOGRAPHY

1. DEUTSCH, F.: *Applied Psychoanalysis*. Grune & Stratton, New York, 1949.
2. CASTIGLIONE, A.: *Adventures of the Mind*. Knopf, New York, 1946.
3. ENGEL, G. L.: The Surrogate Ego Role of the Physician in the Management of the Physically Sick Patient. Read at the Midwinter Meeting of the American Psychoanalytic Association, New York, December, 1951.

4. FREUD, S.: (1910) The Future Prospects of Psycho-Analytic Therapy. *Collected Papers*, 2:285-296. Hogarth Press, London, 1924.
5. FREUD, S.: (1912) The Dynamics of Transference. *Collected Papers*, 2:312-322. Hogarth Press, London, 1924.
6. FREUD, S.: (1912) Recommendations for Physicians on the Psycho-Analytic Method of Treatment. *Collected Papers*, 2:323-333. Hogarth Press, London, 1924.
7. FREUD, S.: (1913) Further Recommendations in the Technique of Psycho-Analysis. On Beginning the Treatment. The Question of the First Communications. The Dynamics of the Cure. *Collected Papers*, 2:342-365. Hogarth Press, London, 1924.
8. FREUD, S.: (1914) Further Recommendations in the Technique of Psycho-Analysis. Recollection, Repetition and Working Through. *Collected Papers*, 2:366-376. Hogarth Press, London, 1924.
9. FREUD, S.: (1915) Further Recommendations in the Technique of Psycho-Analysis. Observations on Transference-Love. *Collected Papers*, 2:377-391. Hogarth Press, London, 1924.
10. FREUD, S.: (1919) Turnings in the Ways of Psycho-Analytic Therapy. *Collected Papers*, 2:392-402. Hogarth Press, London, 1924.
11. FREUD, S.: (1920) *Beyond the Pleasure Principle*. Hogarth Press, London, 1922.
12. FREUD, S.: (1923) *The Ego and the Id*. Hogarth Press, London, 1927.
13. FREUD, S.: (1926) *Inhibition, Symptom and Anxiety*. Hogarth Press, London, Third Impression 1949.
14. FREUD, S.: (1937) Analysis Terminable and Interminable. *Int. J. Psa.*, 18:374, 1937.
15. GRINKER, R. R.: Psychotherapy in Medical and Surgical Hospitals. Read at the Midwinter Meeting of the American Psychoanalytic Association, New York, December, 1951.
16. JANOWITZ, H. D. et al.: A Quantitative Study of the Gastric Secretory Response to Sham Feeding in a Human Subject. *Gastroenterol.*, 16:104-116, 1950.
17. JOSEPH, E. D. et al.: A Psychological Study of Neurodermatitis With a Case Report. *J. Mt. Sinai Hosp.*, 15:360-366, 1949.
18. KAUFMAN, M. R.: Factors in Psychotherapy: A Psychoanalytic Evaluation. *Psychiat. Quart.*, 15:117-142, 1941.
19. KAUFMAN, M. R.: Ill Health As an Expression of Anxiety in a Combat Unit. *Psychosom. Med.*, 9:104-109, 1947.
20. KAUFMAN, M. R., and BEATON, L. E.: A Psychiatric Treatment Program in Combat. *Bull. Menninger Clin.*, 11:1-14, 1947.
21. LEVINE, M.: *Psychotherapy in Medical Practice*. Macmillan, New York, 1942.

22. LUDWIG, A. O.: The Psychotherapy of Rheumatoid Arthritis. Read at the Midwinter Meeting of the American Psychoanalytic Association, New York, December, 1951.
23. MARGOLIN, S. G.: Anaclitic Therapy in Organic Diseases. Read at the Midwinter Meeting of the American Psychoanalytic Association, New York, December, 1951.
24. MARGOLIN, S. G.: Personal Communication.
25. MARGOLIN, S. G., and KAUFMAN, M. R.: What Is Psychosomatic Medicine? *Med. Clin. North Am.*, New York Number, pp. 609-610, May, 1948.
26. MARGOLIN, S. G. et al: Variations of Gastric Functions During Conscious and Unconscious Conflict States. Life Stress and Bodily Disease. *Proc. Assn. Reserach in Nerv. & Ment. Dis.*, 29:656-664, 1950.
27. NUNBERG, H.: Practice and Theory of Psychoanalysis. Nervous and Mental Disease Monograph, No. 74, New York, 1948.
28. SIGERIST, H. E.: *A History of Medicine.* Volume I: Primitive and Archaic Medicine. Oxford University Press, New York, 1951.
29. SYMPOSIUM ON THE EVALUATION OF THERAPEUTIC RESULTS: *Int. J. Psa.*, 29:7-20, 1948; also in *The Yearbook of Psychoanalysis*, 5:11-34. International Universities Press, 1949.
30. SYMPOSIUM ON THE THEORY OF THE THERAPEUTIC RESULTS OF PSYCHOANALYSIS: *Int. J. Psa.*, 18:138-171, 1937.
31. WAELDER, R.: The Principle of Multiple Functions. Observations on Overdetermination. *Psa. Quart.*, 5:45-62, 1936.

DISCUSSION

DR. IVES HENDRICK:

The ultimate problem of psychosomatic medicine is that of selection of organ system in the resolution of emotional conflicts by alteration of normal physiologic function. The best known efforts to answer this problem—that the locale of disease is determinated by the symbolic meaning of the organ, that the organ is fixated by coincidence of systemic disease and emotional conflict during infancy, that each organ activity satisfies specific forms of active or passive emotional needs—all these seem to me pertinent to special cases but do not provide an acceptable generalization. The fantasies, especially unconscious fantasies of patients give us invaluable information as to the specific nature of the crucial conflict, but do not show solely why the tension leads to dysfunction in a specific organ.

I am proposing a hypothesis which has much to recommend it, and does not necessarily contradict those mentioned above. My hypothesis is that the "choice" of organ system is the result of *physiologic infantilism*, or immaturity of homeostatic processes in an organ system. This hypothesis is based upon the fact of physiology that disturbances of homeostasis in infancy normally lead to quantitatively greater reactions than similar stimuli produce in the more mature organism. Thus the heat-regulating mechanism of the definitely premature neonate is poor or absent, whereas it is normally well developed in the full-term baby. Older infants normally show their immaturity of the temperature mechanism by the fact that a disturbance of a given severity, for example, an infection, normally produces a much higher temperature than the same threat does in the older child or adult. The same is true of leukocytic reactions, indeed of all physiologic systems. The preschool child, for example, often reacts normally to relatively mild emotional disturbances, especially the threat of loss of love, by nausea or vomiting—such gastric disturbances at an early age are often the equivalent of mental depression in later years. The electroencephalogram illustrates this principle in another system where physiologic maturity is established still later; brain waves of the normal child are not stabilized patterns like those of adults, and frequently reveal in normal children waves which would be characteristic of epilepsy in maturity.

My hypothesis is that psychosomatic diseases are based upon a physiologic lability of the autonomic nervous system normally found at immature development levels, and that these phenomena might well be considered another type of the regression or fixation at an infantile functional level with which we are familiar in the mental characteristics of the psychoneuroses. The hypothesis can, therefore, appropriately be referred to as the *principle of physiologic infantilism, and defined as the tendency to discharge conflict in those organs where the physiologic lability of normal immaturity has been retained or can be established.*[1]

[1] "Synopsis of Psychosomatic Diagnosis and Treatment," Flanders Dunbar, M.D., Editor, C. V. Mosby Co., 1948. pp. 55-6.

DR. BERNARD BANDLER:

Dr. Hendrick has raised the most basic and general theoretical problem of psychosomatic medicine and he has introduced a hypothesis to answer it. The question he asks can be paraphrased: how is psychosomatic medicine possible; what assumption or assumptions must we make to account for it? This question is far more general than that of the choice of a particular organ or organ system, the problem of specificity. In the field of the neuroses, specificity would refer to the choice of the neuroses; the comparable general question would be: what general theoretical assumption must we make to account for the neuroses at all?

In a way the problem is easier for the neuroses because the clinical phenomena and diagnostic syndromes, in spite of overlap, are fairly clearly demarcated. With psychosomatic medicine the problem is more complicated because there is less clarity and agreement about what is to be explained. Is it simply a group of disease entities, of unknown etiology, in which psychological factors play a significant role; the group of familiar diseases such as ulcerative colitis, asthma, etc.? Or does our concept of psychosomatic medicine cover all diseases, including the neuroses and psychoses?

Dr. Hendrick starts from the conviction, which I share, that the hypotheses that we employ for the neuroses and psychoses are inadequate to account for the complete clinical picture which we see in psychosomatic disease, however significant they are for our psychological understanding of it. The final solution is not to be found solely in terms of ego development and of the

141

vicissitudes of the libidinal and aggressive instincts. Even if we had, for example, complete understanding of the obscure preverbal larval period of early differentiation of the ego from the id, and from the mother, and from the environment, and of the development of the body image, at the time when the primary process was dominant and the pleasure principle prevailed, we would still be confronted with the basic problem of psychosomatic disease. Another set of factors, the somatic, the physiological, must be taken into account.

The attempt to account for the somatic factor by the concurrence of physical disease with early developmental conflicts Dr. Hendrick rules out as too special and accidental. Although he does not mention heredity and constitution, I believe they can be ruled out too, since they, along with concurrent disease, presuppose a general physiological hypothesis, and would seem rather to account for fixation. Dr. Hendrick offers the hypothesis of physiological infantilism, and its persistence or the regression to it, as a prerequisite for our understanding of psychosomatic medicine. This concept is not advanced as an alternative to our other theories but rather as the substructure into which they are to be interpreted. The concept, I believe, can easily be aligned into the framework of Freud's psychosomatic definition of instinct as a borderland concept, and his belief that ultimately our theory of instincts will rest on a biological foundation.

In trying to survey some of the problems raised by this hypothesis there are certain questions which I should like to ask. Since there is regression to physiological infantilism there must be fixation. What then is the mechanism or mechanisms by which physiological fixation takes place? So far we have merely shifted the problem of psychosomatic medicine from the psychological realm to the physiological and reformulated it in physiological terms. Does physiological fixation take place because of the psychological factors as being insufficient by themselves to account for psychosomatic medicine, or because of heredity, constitution and concomitant disease; or by a summation of all these factors within the physiological matrix?

A problem related to fixation is that of the relationship of physiological regression to instinctual and ego regression. To what extent do they influence each other; to what extent do they go hand in hand; and to what extent and under what condition may they proceed relatively independently? For example, in hypochrondiasis we see a profound ego and instinctual regression without apparent physiological regression. We know that within clinical types of psychosomatic disease we see great variation in intactness of personality, and ego strength. Does that mean that patients with the same disease entity, showing great variability in ego and libidio organization and degree of regression, all regress to the same level of physiological infantilism? Lastly we see certain severe psychosomatic entities, such as ulcerative colitis, where ego, instinctual and physiological regression proceed more synchronously and where reversibility to psychosis is not infrequent. Or are there degrees and stages of physiological organization permitting of various points of fixation?

There are other questions which call for further elaboration: What are the general intermediary processes and mechanisms which lead from physiological regression to pathological disease? Why does not a patient, for example, who develops ulcerative colitis, remain instead at the level of infantile bowel physiology? The answer, I believe, would be an economic one: namely, that the infantile homeostasis with its lability and greater reactions to stimuli breaks down under the quantity of discharge from conflict, a quantity to which the infant is not subjected.

Dr. Joseph J. Michaels:

The hypothesis that the "choice" of organ system is the result of "physiologic infantilism," or immaturity of homeostatic processes in an organic system, is based upon the fact of physiology that disturbances of homeostasis in infancy normally lead to quantitatively greater reactions than similar stimuli produced in the more mature organism. The hypothesis can, therefore, as we have heard, appropriately be referred to as the principle of physiologic infantilism, and defined as the tendency to discharge conflict in those organs where the physiologic lability of normal immaturity has been retained or can be established.

It is gratifying to find that one's speculations are confirmed independently by different investigators who use different approaches and methods. The conception of physiological infantilism I have thought of as physiological regression and so have Drs. Margolin and Grinker. While in the Army where one can be more venturesome, I wrote a paper entitled "A Psychiatric Adventure in Comparative Pathophysiology of the Infant and Adult—With Some Theoretical Suggestions in Regard to Regression in Somatic Visceral Functions."[1]

Therefore, I should like to discuss briefly the following viewpoints: (1) Freud's conception of psychological regression and Child's principle of the gradient; (2) the principle of homeostasis; (3) anxiety; (4) clinical examples; (5) choice of organ neurosis; and (6) the validation of the hypothesis.

(1) *Freud's conception of psychological regression and Child's gradient.*—The question arose that just as one finds regressive phenomena psychologically, might one not find this true physiologically? Is it possible to regard the somatic expression of a psychological disorder as a regression of the adult physiological level to an infantile physiological level. Similar conceptions are found in neurology, where Hughlings Jackson has written on "Evolution and Dissolution of the Central Nervous System" which was applied primarily to the highest levels.

Grinker indicated that repression and inhibition, which are basic principles in psychoanalysis and neurology, respectively, are dynamically identical. It is of some interest that in neurology, regression was first investigated primarily in the higher levels of neurophysiologic functions, whereas Freud's contributions began primarily at the lower levels. The physiologist, C. M. Child, emphasizing the principle of the gradient, stated that "In all forms in which differentiation occurs readily, the physiologically isolated part loses, to a greater or lesser extent, its differentiation as a part, and returns to or approaches an embryonic condition."

[1] *J. Nerv. & Ment. Dis.,* 100:49, 1944.

(2) *The principle of homeostasis.*—Cannon believes that there is an absence or deficiency of homeostatic regulation in babies during a considerable period after birth and during the later, rather slow acquirement of control. From psychoanalytic experience, we know that there are fluctuations in the balance of instinctual forces and the control agencies during the periods of infancy, puberty, and involution. From a physiological standpoint, it might be anticipated that these later age periods similarly evoke the basic physiological patterns established in infancy and early childhood. You will recall that Dr. Margolin referred to the homeostatic funnel, the base of which is broad in infancy and restricts with age. It would be of interest to determine experimentally whether this homeostatic funnel varies and fluctuates in its circumference during these changing, critical age periods. Infancy is a most vulnerable period of life with the greatest degree of variability and lability.

(3) *Anxiety.*—The somatic accompaniments of anxiety seem to resemble an accentuated physiological state of infancy. It is my impression that the startle state that is present in infancy, is the result of the psychobiological separation of the fetus from the mother.

(4) *Clinical examples.*—With the above ideas in mind, I reviewed some of the literature on the psychobiological state in infancy and described the variations which occur in the different systems under the following headings: (a) autonomic nervous system, endocrine and electrolytic milieu, regulation of water and mineral balance, body temperature and the blood; (b) cardiores-

piratory; (c) gastrointestinal; (d) genitourinary; (e) muscles, bones and joints; (f) skin.

From a clinical standpoint, I would like to present a few examples from the cardiorespiratory and gastrointestinal systems. In infancy there is an increased tendency toward spasm as manifested in laryngeal spasm, stridor and wheezing. It does not seem fortuitous that the type of contagious disease involving the respiratory system which afflicts the infant and young child, should be whooping cough. In infancy, there is much yawning, sighing, sneezing, variations in the rate and rhythm of both the cardiac and respiratory functions. In states of anxiety, sighing and variations in the rate, rhythm and depth of respiration occur. Variations in the pulse rate, rhythm, blood pressure, extrasytoles are very common in individuals with neuroses and especially in the state of anxiety.

Another example is from the gastrointestinal tract. One of the most common somatic manifestations of anxiety in adults is diarrhea. In fact, in the condition of mucous colitis, the type of digestive disturbances is reminiscent of the infant's type of digestion with its frequent stools and soft water consistency. One might postulate that this symptom is a return to a less differentiated functioning of the gastrointestinal tract which was appropriate for infancy but is discordant for the mature functioning of the gastrointestinal tract of the adult. The syndrome of the spastic colon with its disturbance in tone, spasms in some segments, and dilatation in others, colic, cramps and spastic constipation, would be another example of a type of function which was considered more appropriate for infancy and childhood. In individuals with gastrointestinal neuroses, the presence of aerophagia, belching, hiccuping, vomiting, distention, colic, etc., may seem to be a revival of the type of dysfunctions ordinarily present in infancy and childhood.

(5) *The choice of the organ in organ neuroses.*—Deutsch, in 1939, suggested that "the organ involved is determined by the fact that it was originally affected at a time antedating the full evolution of instinctual life." From the above conceptions it would appear that the choice of the organ or system may also be dependent upon the fusion of an emotional process at a labile period when the organ or system had not yet attained its full maturation. Thus there is a fusion of immature psychological events and immature physiological processes.

(6) *Validation of hypothesis.*—Although it is realized that many of the conceptions described have been derived from analogies and parallels, it might be possible to prove them experimentally. (a) For example, an adult patient with psychoneurotic states, in whom the symptoms are predominantly of a somatic visceral nature, could be studied in terms of the extent to which the physiological changes observed in the adult are comparable to an accentuation of the physiological state which is encountered in the newborn or in the infant. (b) If detailed investigation of the psychosomatic reactions of infants and preschool children, as to the specific organ and organ systems were made, and at a later date, in adolescence and adulthood, longitudinal follow-up studies were carried out, then information would be obtained as to the vicissitudes of the psychosomatic symptoms. Finally (c) it may be that a psycho-

148

somatic quotient could be established by dividing the level of immature somatic functioning by the level of mature somatic functioning. I would like to consider the possibility of changing the name of the hypothesis "infantile physiology" to "physiologic regression." Such a change in name would be more consistent with psychoanalytic theory and terminology and would avoid the prejudicial aspects of the word "infantile."

Dr. Elizabeth Zetzel:

I was extremely stimulated not only by the individual papers as such, but by a consideration of the relationship between them and the new light thrown on our approach to psychosomatic illness.

I think it will clarify my contribution if I begin by stating those aspects of the panel which raised most questions in my mind; namely, first, the potential light these investigations and hypotheses may throw on the important question as to the role played by constitutional factors in the predisposition to physical and mental disease and, second, the possible implication for therapy of new discoveries made in this connection.

It might simplify my argument if I state very briefly my own interpretation of the hypothesis put forward, which is to the effect that concurrent and inextricably bound up with the early psychological development, there is a physiological development with equally definite progressive stages (described by Dr. Margolin as involuntary, combined, and voluntary). Similarly, in addition, it is suggested that in psychosomatic disease a regressive process takes place, with the emergence of

149

physiological responses, which, although they had been appropriate to the infantile situation, are no more appropriate to the adult than are the parallel manifestations of psychological regression. It is, moreover, impossible to separate the psychological from the physiological functions so that, on the one hand, profound physiological regressions predominantly precipitated by psychological events, and on the other hand, certain psychological manifestations of serious physical illnesses are *both* characterized by the appropriate physical and psychological symptomatology. In short, the psychotic features which have been recognized in certain serious psychosomatic diseases confirm the evidence that, in these illnesses, physiological regression to the mechanisms of a very early infantile level has taken place.

As a working hypothesis toward the confirmation of which a good deal of suggestive evidence has already been offered, I find this thesis most attractive and stimulating. I am concerned not to criticize it but to raise certain problems which have occurred to me, in particular in regard to the problems of predisposition and prognosis. Perhaps I might frame my question by referring briefly to another of the symposium papers, Dr. Gerard's, which seemed to me to offer an important complement to that of Dr. Margolin. Dr. Gerard's findings, like those of Dr. Spitz, and from another point of view those of the English school, all stress the decisive importance of the early mother-child relationship for future mental and physical health. In this connection, for example, I would like to refer to a paper by Dr. Winnicott, in which he described schizophrenia as a deficiency disease. Granted, however, that we can see in the type of case she quotes, the probably close relationship of psychosomatic disease to *real* experiences of deprivation and frustration, I think we still have to remember: (a) that many children with equally traumatic experiences do *not* develop psychosomatic disease but rather develop psychological deviations often the precursors of psychotic illness in adult life; (b) that the basic psychotic pathology of psychosomatic patients is usually revealed *after* improvement of the physical condition; (c) that psychosomatic disease, at least of the seriously regressive type associated with psychotic psychopathology, is relatively uncommon in the clinical psychotic; (d) that psychotic patients frequently show transient improvement and even recovery during a serious physical illness.

I am particularly interested here in raising questions:

1. To what extent does the predisposition to psychosomatic disease (rather than psychosis) depend on the occurrence during infancy of specific *physical* traumatic experiences which result in physiological fixation points at a primitive level, similar to the psychological fixation points we premise for psychotic illnesses?

2. Can this hypothesis account for all cases, or do we need to premise in addition some innate factor, presumably constitutional, which renders certain individuals less able than others to attain, in situations of physical stress however produced, homeostasis?

3. If we premise some constitutional factor, should we consider it to be specific for psychosomatic disease, i.e., physiological, or should we rather premise some common factor which could produce in a predisposed individual either psychosis or psychosomatic disease, in

which the course of events is determined by the specific life experiences and dynamic development which will lead on the one hand to psychotic illness, and on the other to psychosomatic disease?

This relates closely to the question I raised here two years ago in connection with the capacity to bear anxiety when I suggested that the predisposition to psychosis might be related to a deficency in this tolerance. I bring this question up not only because of its relevance to the problem of genesis, but also because it seems to me to be of decisive importance in our attitude toward therapy. Assuming for the moment that the premature experience of an intolerable degree of anxiety may determine the predisposition to psychosis or psychosomatic disease, we will also have to premise, just as with adult neurotics, prognostic differences according to the extent of the traumatic experience undergone. At one extreme, that is to say, we might place the group of severely frustrated and deprived children described by Dr. Gerard; at the other, I believe we must consider the possibility of severely predisposed infants who react to such frustrations as are inevitable in even the best environment with an equal tolerance. The anaclitic type of therapy described by Drs. Margolin and Kaufman rests, or so it seems to me, on the hypothesis that the predisposition to psychosomatic disease and to psychosis depends, much as Winnicott suggested, on a deficiency of infantile gratification. Whether the granting of this gratification in adult life will facilitate some progressive alteration will, however, or so it seems to me, depend on the potentialities of the individual for developing an increased capacity to bear frustration.

This does not in any way minimize the value of this therapy as a life-saving device in the severely ill patients to whom Dr. Margolin refers. It does, however, raise a question as to how far the anaclitic type of treatment can result in permanent beneficial effects on patients whose symptomatology is based on an irreversible and possibly constitutional deficiency in the capacity to bear frustration and anxiety.

I have obviously simplified this problem very considerably for purposes of discussion. It seems to me, however, that it is in the answers to this question which are being sought by the members of this panel in relation to psychosomatic disease, and by the many who are investigating the potentialities for psychotherapy in psychotic patients, that we may ultimately find an answer to many of these difficult problems regarding the role played by constitution and environment in the development of physical and mental disease.

To sum up: I have attempted to apply Dr. Margolin's and Dr. Hendrick's very stimulating hypothesis regarding the part played by physiological regression to a consideration of the relationship of physical and psychological factors in determining the type of illness developed by a predisposed individual. I have briefly considered the nature of the predisposition and suggested a common factor related to the capacity to bear frustration, whether mainly experienced as physical or emotional. Finally, I have suggested that the response to anaclitic therapy may throw further light on the relative part played by constitutional and environmental factors in the predisposition to these diseases.

DR. GRETE L. BIBRING:

Of special interest to me is the analysis of the scientific milieu in which Dr. Margolin's significant paper (and most of the papers read at the Symposium, but especially Dr. Grinker's contribution) could develop. This milieu is provided by:

1. The psychoanalytic observations of early childhood which are increasingly gaining in importance at child study centers;
2. The findings in the field of ego psychology;
3. The work of Selye on stress;
4. Last, not least, the ancient mind-body problem which has been revived intensely by the growing interest in psychosomatic concepts.[1]

This atmosphere of common interests made our panel so interesting and integrated the different contributions so well.

Dr. Margolin used already in his paper "Some Metapsychological Aspects of Psychosomatic Medicine," which he read to the Boston Psychoanalytic Society on October 4, 1950, an approach which differed considerably from the more traditional attempts to establish the specificity of psychosomatic symptoms and conditions. He introduced into the discussion of the different patterns of physiological data which he could observe, the more general psychological concepts like instinctual break-through, reaction formation, defenses, instead of the usual more detailed and specific concepts of, for instance, anger, or need for love, or dependency. This seemed to me a most important step in the direction of

[1] Gerard, R. W. Physiology and Psychiatry, *Am. J. Psychiat.*, 1949.

his present work. In keeping with the nonspecific approach, Dr. Margolin is attempting to isolate the pathogenic process within the wide area of combinations of different developmental conditions, correlating the somatic and ego development. In outlining the phases of this maturation process, the major emphasis lies with the postnatal, preverbal period characterized by global reactions to stimuli, primitive affects, fluctuating ego boundaries, lack of control over motor reactions, i.e., involuntary reactions.[2]

The further development consists in the establishment of defined ego boundaries, of voluntary control over motor reactions, in the acceptance of the reality principle, in the formation of language and the like. This process of developing functions is accompanied by the changing "fantasies of functions" which comprise the important experiences along this process, influenced by their psychological significance. The paper further attempts to point out danger zones for organ fixation:

1. Where ego boundaries are prematurely established (through early introduction of the reality principle);

2. When the voluntary control of motor reaction is forced before its time;

3. Where fusions of involuntary and voluntary processes occur.

[2] In keeping with my introductory remarks about the significant investigation in this direction, see Edward Glover's article on "Functional Aspects of the Mental Apparatus," *Int. J. Psychoanal.*, 1950. Here Glover arrives at conclusions which come rather close to Margolin's and Grinker's point of view. "The first mental disorders at this primary functional stage are simple disorders of excitation and discharge without fixed psychological content giving rise to the purest form of psychosomatic reactions (disturbances of affects of organ innervations, of motor discharge, of sleep)."

The psychosomatic symptom is viewed as the result of the regressive disintegration of the acquired centrally organized control, of the differentiated affects, of the stable homeostatic boundaries, and of the corresponding advanced fantasies of functions. This disintegration revives the primitive global reactions for which the aging tissue has lost its adaptation; thus the somatic components of these regressively reëstablished primordial affects lead to the psychosomatic disorder. The therapy which Dr. Margolin applies is closely related to his theoretical concepts: with the help of anaclitic gratifications, with which the therapist follows the patient into his state of primitive needs and emotions, a change of mood can be achieved, and with it remission will be introduced.

It seems to me that this interesting system of theory and technique integrates comprehensively the prevailing therapeutic trends which replaced increasingly the straight insight therapy of the earlier era in psychosomatic medicine, and, beyond it, it opens new ways for the understanding and treatment of these disorders.

In discussing the different propositions in the paper, which seem apt to raise questions or to lead to new trends of ideas, I will restrict myself to those points which have, in my opinion, significant implications:

1. One problem which appears not sufficiently included in Dr. Margolin's presentation, refers to the incident of psychosomatic disturbances in young children. For this age group, the pathogenic effect of the primitive global reactions cannot equally be explained by the incompatibility between these primitive affects and the stabilized, rigid system and functions of the

156

later life periods. It therefore seems necessary to consider additional etiological factors, like erogenicity, traumatic fixation and the like, which then, in turn, have to be considered just as well in the etiology of the adult psychosomatic case.[3]

2. As far as I can see, Dr. Margolin introduces a new form of early, undifferentiated affects in contradistinction to the later mature forms, a viewpoint which needs more clarification, as it introduces a modification of the present theory of affects.

3. The most important problem lies, in my opinion, in the implications this system has on the concept of transference management in psychoanalytic treatment. Dr. Margolin's idea, if understood in its full meaning, implies that only relatively late childhood conflicts—approximately of the order of hysteria—can be treated primarily on the basis of insight therapy. Not only psychosomatic cases (and probably psychoses) but a large variety of early fixated psychoneuroses would have to be reached first on the basis of instinctual (or need) gratification, i.e., transference manipulation, and only then insight therapy could be applied. This comes very close to Ferenczi's technique,[4] and introduces Michael Balint's concepts[5] of the "new beginning" in analysis.

[3] Deutsch, F. Choice of the Organ in Organ Neurosis. *Int. J. Psychoanal.*, XX, 1939; *idem*, Psychosomatic Aspects of Dermatology. *Nerv. Child*, V, 1945.

[4] Ferenczi, S. The Principle of Relaxation and Neocatharsis. *Int. J. Psychoanal.*, XI, 1930; *idem*, Child Analysis in the Analysis of Adults. *Ibid.*, XII, 1931.

[5] Balint, M. Charateranalyse und Neubeginn. *Int. Ztschr. f. Psychoanal.*, XX, 1933.

Dr. Felix Deutsch:

The basic question in Dr. Kubie's paper is in his words: "What is there which is of a peculiar or special or different or *specific* nature about the regression or disassociative processes which result in physiological disturbances?" Dr. Kubie leaves this question unanswered, but tries to disprove the concept of specificity by pointing out all the possible variations which play a role in every symptom formation. The fact cannot be argued that not any neurotic symptom is reducible to a single and constant group of determinants, but it is rather the constellation of functional symptoms which constitute the dynamic units. This constellation develops slowly with specific determinants until the causal chain is closed. The grouping of these determinants can be traced back on a path which determines the specificity of the ultimate symptom. The reappearance of the symptom will always be due to a trigger situation which set the dynamics of the specific symptom in motion. This view strongly contradicts Dr. Kubie's statement that the choice of the organ is dependent in very large part upon almost accidental factors in the final common path.

By and large, all symptoms are always overdetermined, but there is likewise always a focal point around which the "satellites" contribute their part. In brief, the principles of the development of psychosomatic symptoms are:

1. An organic functional disorder in the earliest childhood, sometimes originating on a genetic basis.
2. Deviation and fixation of instinctual drives during

the earliest psychic development, and fusion of these with the different sense perceptions related to this specific organ system, being used by the ego for the pathological conflict solutions.

3. Complementary neurotic traits of the enviroment which decreased the strength of the ego.

Dr. Kubie raises the question how the occurrence of two or more kinds of psychosomatic disorders in the same person can be explained, if for each of them specific determinants should be necessary. In order to reconcile these apparent contradictions, we have to assume that each of these particular disorders occurred in different periods of psychic development, let us say a respiratory one on the oral level, a skin affliction on the narcissistic level. It could also be that the occurrence of the organic process might have led to a regression, or might have happened on the occasion when the ego had regressive tendencies toward those particular levels and seized the opportunity for the retreat. The specificity of the trigger situations in reality will then explain why once one and why once the other condition appears. This variability of a psychosomatic symptom complex suggests a brittle ego, which in its development was, on the one hand, in greater need of defenses, and on the other hand, experienced the danger to its bodily integrity in a compliant conflict situation, e.g., the skin affliction appeared at a time just when the ego appealed to the narcissism for its self-assertion, or the respiratory process occurred in an occasion of frustration which inspired the ego to look for oral gratification.

It cannot be emphasized strongly enough that it is always the psychic representation of the disturbed function, viz., the body image, which is shaken in its foundation, and that the ego has to call upon all its resources to restore the integrity of this image. By and large, the blow will be felt most severely by those functional systems which have been the pillars of the body ego. For this reason, the study of a specific organic disease entity from an analytic point of view has to break up this entity—which is only one from a medical point of view —into its functional and formative components for an understanding of their psychic representation, and for an evaluation of the part it plays in motivating psychodynamically the specific formation of the disease entity. If one does not adhere to this psychosomatic concept, then problems are set for correlation which do not belong together at all, or only indirectly. This kind of research is outdated and should be replaced by applied-analytic methods of psychosomatic investigation.

In regard to Kubie's basic question about the choice of the organ, which he modestly left unanswered, I may repeat the suggestions I made fourteen years ago:

The choice of the organ depends on:

1. occurrence of an organic dysfunction (hyper or hypo) in the neonatal or early infancy period;
2. on the coincidence of this dysfunction with instinctual conflicts on the specific level of psychic development;
3. on the frequency of the simultaneous repetition of this dysfunction and of the specific conflict;
4. to what extent and how many sense perceptions became involved in the psychosomatic process;
5. on the fusion of these two processes;

6. on the repression of the original experience which provoked the conflict;
7. on the consistency of using the organic dysfunction as the preverbal expression of the repressed conflicts and their related memories;
8. on factors and figures in the environment which stimulate the specific conflict;
9. on the early symbolization and personification of these figures in the parts of the body involved;
10. on the degree of the ego weakness and its inability of solving the conflicts otherwise;
11. on the degree of the resulting ego defect and organic defect;
12. on the type of behavior disorder or neurosis which has finally developed;
13. on the type of neurosis of the parental and family figures;
14. on other incidental and accidental life experiences.

DR. LUCIE JESSNER:

To test and prove her theory—i.e., that maladaptation of an organ may arise from emotional difficulties experienced in the first months of life, when patterns of response are initiated—Dr. Gerard analyzed detailed behavior of mothers in the care of their children to determine the influence upon ego development of minute variations in the mode of feeding, of holding, of supporting, of bathing, of talking or singing, of smiling or frowning, and also the influence of the consistency or lack of consistency of these actions. It seems to Dr. Gerard that from such data one might find the answer to questions of choice of symptoms and of personality characteristics which have evaded explanation from gross descriptions of environmental experiences.

She states that there was "an important general characteristic which all these cases had in common with each other and with all the cases in the study which presented various psychotic-like symptoms. With no exception, all these mothers were narcissistic, uninterested in the child except as a self-enhancing asset, resented the exertion involved in child care, and rarely gained pleasure from the mother-child relationship. In other words, they all lacked motherliness. Most were rejecting and physically cruel in various ways."

Here, unfortunately, Dr. Gerard's paper ended, probably because of limitation of time. I felt the most important device of her study was the "attempt to analyze detailed behavior of mothers" and I regret that she had to summarize her findings in general terms. I was greatly stimulated by her talk, but also felt frustrated not to hear about her detailed findings. For instance, it appeared most relevant when she spoke of consistency and inconsistency in mothers' behavior. It seems to me that consistent neglect, withdrawal or coldness will keep the infant in steady emotional starvation, not permitting the child to cathect the mother with feelings and thus may lead to the development of an atypical child, whereas inconsistency and ambivalence tend to arouse expectations which ever so often are not fulfilled, thus disturbing patterns of biologic response, a condition probably important for the development of psychosomatic illnesses.

One other attitude of the mother, overgratification of

needs, may lead to a lessening of incentive, activity and requests, and to a lowering of tension, and this probably influences biologic responses. Also the mother's attitude toward special functions or parts of the body deserves closer study, e.g., Phyllis Greenacres' paper on over-stimulation of the genitals and its effect on the personality development is an important step in that direction.

It also seems relevant in following Dr. Gerard's proposition of a detailed study to look at the mother-child relationship not as a one-sided affair, not as a monologue but a dialogue, and to take into account the individual responsiveness of the infant to his mother. It seems that needs of infants for tenderness, for stimulation or protection from stimuli vary from one individual to the other, just as the requests for amount and frequency of feeding is variable.

It seems likewise essential to observe closely the development and the fluctuation in the mother-child relationship, and not to take this constellation as a state unit; e.g., an illness, as often has been pointed out, can bring decisive alteration. In any longer illness we so frequently see that in the beginning attention to the child is increased and the patient becomes the center of the family. If the child does not get well soon, anger, resentment and guilt feelings are often aroused in the mother and in turn felt by the child, which feels deprived of his secondary gain. This may be the moment when feeding difficulties and depression start.

From our studies on children with psychosomatic diseases at the Massachusetts General Hospital, I cannot confirm the general characteristics of the "narcissistic" mother. In a group of nineteen children with rheumatoid arthritis, Dr. Gaston Blom and Miss Grace Nichols found the mothers depressive, in a slave-like bondage with the sick child and with guilt feelings focused on the pregnancy with the patient. We also observed that mothers of asthmatic children did not represent a special type, but that in this group displacement of feelings (e.g., toward a younger sibling) on the patient played a crucial role.

I think that our future studies on psychosomatic patients will follow Dr. Gerard's suggestion for detailed observation, and will lead away from a "specificity" of mothers toward more individualized findings of the interplay between mother and child.

Dr. Lydia G. Dawes:

Dr. Gerard's paper was very stimulating to all of us working in the children's field. She tries first of all to reconstruct the normal patterns, and emphasizes the specific condition "symbiosis" which is found in the mother-child relationship. She sketches the development of the child and then describes what the mothers looked like who had sick children. She establishes a correlation between the sick children and the attitudes of the mothers who cared for them. This paper is important as well as thought-provoking.

In the discussion of her cases, Dr. Gerard stated that they were all under twelve. Could she give us more details as to age and appearance of the symptoms? Perhaps she could break down this large age group into smaller groups, with special attention to the transitional points in early development of each child. Perhaps she could define "symbiosis" more specifically since the dependence of the healthy infant and young child on the mother extends over a period of years, and to a certain extent throughout all of childhood.

When does the "symbiotic" relationship become so dangerous to the child that it may cause illness? Could she give us more detailed information on this point? I suspect that this was an oversight and that her observations on both healthy and sick children might clarify the matter. In other words, how does the mother's attitude influence the child? How does the child influence the mother, so that this early, close relationship is no longer necessary? How do the mothers of sick children differ from the mothers of healthy children, who progress steadily forward along their developmental curves? Research along these lines is going on at the Children's Center, the Children's Hospital and the Wellesley project.

For example, in the Wellesley study of the preschool group (four- to five-year-olds), we noted that many of these sick children seemed to use their symptoms in the same way that healthy children use play, i.e., to master a frustrating reality. Freud noted that whenever the organism is flooded with a very large quantity of excitation, it attempts to get rid of this by subsequent active repetitions of the situation that induced the excessive excitation. This takes place in the early games of little children and in their dreams as well.

We observed that the children suffering from asthma, ulcerative colitis, encopresis, cyclic vomiting, etc., had no energy for playing—it seemed to be used up by the sick process. According to our experience the improvement in symptoms was accompanied by the appearance of play patterns characteristic for these age groups.

What part does the child play in eliciting response from the mother? Some children in the early latency group (six to eight years) with psychosomatic symptoms, verbalized clearly that they did not worry about the illness; e.g., one child in analysis said, "My mother worries about my asthma. I don't like it, but I have it. She gets anxious when I get sick. I am not anxious." Others resented their mother's care, but continually asked for her help when ill, and were negative and hostile to their mothers during exacerbations of illness.

Also, to my surprise, the fathers were not mentioned by Dr. Gerard. But doesn't the father also influence the mother-child relationship? Many young fathers are intensely jealous of the baby. They resent it and are openly hostile when the mother cares for the baby. These mothers are in severe conflict and must not only master new tasks, but deal with the husband's jealousy. They are increasingly anxious because the baby takes so much time and spoils the marital relationship.

We also noted that the father influences the child's attitude toward the symptoms. For instance, we have in treatment a boy of nine who is a soiler. His father continually frustrated the mother's efforts to help the boy overcome this habit by saying that he himself had soiled until he was twelve, and that the boy would get over it, and that she should just clean up after him. We saw a similar attitude in several fathers with bed-wetters. The fathers in these cases actually gave permission to the child to continue his symptoms, saying that they suffered the same way, and the symptom disappeared when they reached twelve.

Everyone is constantly made aware of the multiplicity of facts and the number of crosscurrents in the emotional life surrounding each child, sick or well. Hence, we cannot help being somewhat skeptical about the possibility of typing mothers and drawing conclusions as to the kind of sickness their children will develop. Such correlation of personality types with the occurrence of specific psychosomatic diseases in adults is found in the early studies of Dunbar and others.

I may be wrong, but the correlation of the mother's cruelty and aggression with a specific illness in the child seems too isolated a formulation. I wish we could have more material. For example, how are these feelings of the mother mobilized—by her husband, by her child, or by her own neurosis? Are the observable reactions of the mother a cover for deeper disturbances? What is the significance of actual fatigue, frustration and helplessness in the mobilization of hostile feelings of a mother whose child suffers from chronic disease?

One more point which was not mentioned: what is the unconscious symbolic meaning of the child for the mother? Is the child equated in the mother's unconscious with a stool, a penis, or a narcissistic extension of the self?

In closing, I would like to thank Dr. Gerard for this important contribution, because it points the way especially for work in preventive medicine.

DR. WILLIAM F. MURPHY:

In this discussion, I would like to echo a statement from Dr. Kaufman's paper and amplify it somewhat. I refer to his remark that "we must be careful that the fascination of new observations in ancillary fields does not result in a jettisoning of what has already been won through the painstaking work of years."

In the past five years at Cushing Hospital, we have had extensive experience in treating psychosomatic cases with the sector psychotherapy method of Dr. Deutsch, which we feel is the most scientific and economic way of applying fundamental, empirically developed, and time-tested psychoanalytic principles. We heartily agree with Dr. Kaufman's conclusion that "hypothetically, psychoanalysis with whatever flexibility may be necessary in the individual case, is the only definite etiological treatment in psychosomatic illness." In our opinion, most of the flexibility necessary in each case is more a function of the personality differences and preferences of the therapist than of anything else. We have continued to use sector psychotherapy also because of its teaching value. The problems that we have encountered in dealing with psychosomatic disease from the standpoint of therapy have differed little from those met with in the treatment of any of the neuroses.

I am sure that just as many of our cases of conversion reaction have shown evidence of an underlying narcissistic neurosis or psychosis as have cases of psychosomatic disorders. We heartily agree with Dr. Engel that the physician functions as a surrogate ego during the patient's illness, and especially stress the point that for a physician to function rationally as a surrogate ego, he must understand not only the psychological problems but the nature of the multiple elements that comprise the patient's ego. The source of this understanding continues to be the patient's verbalization. The main task of therapy in psychosomatic disorders also remains essentially the unraveling of a complicated series of anxiety-laden introjections and projections, plus a continual effort to strengthen the adult observing and synthesizing portion of the ego. In this sense, the surrogate ego should be a supplementary aid to this synthesizing portion of the ego. In sector therapy, the strengthening of the synthetic function of the ego and the gratification of the need for causality go hand in hand. These goals can be achieved only when the meaning of the symptom has been determined in terms of intra-ego and interpersonal relationships, as related to present and past experiences.

The strengthening of the synthesizing portion of the ego and attainment of an increase in intrapsychic overall perspective appear to go together with an ability to curb the ego representatives of the instinctual wishes and tyrannical superego figures, and are always accompanied by a reduction in anxiety and a more equitable distribution of defenses against remaining anxiety, so that one organ system or type of defense is not overloaded. The use of a psychosomatic illness as a defense is apparently tied up with the presence of lacunae in the integration of ego components. In some way, the psychosomatic disease functions as the visceral or autonomic nervous system concomitant and representative of the lacunae. With an increase in over-all perspective or strengthening of the synthetic forces of the ego, these lacunae shrink, the disease process abates, and the ability is attained to express affect over a wider range of bodily mechanisms. Here, of course, we are talking about one aspect of the mechanism of denial and what Rene Laforge has called scotomatization. Deutsch has stated it somewhat differently when he says that "the goal of sector psychotherapy in psychosomatic disease is to loosen psychosomatic fusions, to rid the organ system from its old psychic entanglements and from unconscious pathological instinctual influences in order to safeguard the biological functions." It is the presence of these "entanglements" which makes possible a certain type of denial which we speak of as lacunae in the integration of ego components.

One of the criticisms that we have frequently heard concerning sector therapy is that it is too unsubtle and even sadistic. This is an erroneous impression, based mainly upon the difficulties of beginners and has nothing to do with obedience to basic principles. For instance, we try not to allow our guilt feelings over being doctors, or our empathy with the patient, to interfere with our scientific and psychiatric acumen. A cold can, of course, be treated with aspirin and fluids, but a good therapist keeps in mind the feelings of being depressed and unloved that go with the statement, "I have a cold," even though his own nose is running and the entire ward be laid up with the same illness.

As practically every individual is undeveloped and regressed in some sectors of ego functioning, we do not attempt character analysis but confine our efforts to the problems as developed through the key words relating

170

to the patient's organ symptoms. In regard to Dr. Margolin's total therapeutic approach, from the contradictory nature of the ego elements encountered in therapy, it is very difficult for us to understand how anyone can routinely assume a role of total permissiveness, or how a tendency to regress on the part of the patient can be thwarted or not thwarted. The very nature of the conflict makes any attempt to pay Paul mean a robbing of Peter. For the same reason, we are unable to understand such a thing as a demand-feeding schedule, as the demands are always contradictory ones. In sector psychotherapy, no attempt is made to indulge either the infantile ego, the instincts, or the introjected parental aspects of the ego, except when absolutely necessary to preserve a therapeutic relationship, and only when the therapist is aware of the relation between the various ego elements. In sector therapy, our concern is not with the projections and introjections of the patient per se. These are present in everyone, just as in everyone there is a constant shifting between narcissistic and anaclitic relationships. Our concern is rather with the fact that too much anxiety is connected with these necessities, and we try to maintain as our goal the reduction of this anxiety through the strengthening of the synthesizing ego. I might add that we are not unacquainted with demand-feeding schedules in the Veterans Administration and feel that as a general rule an attempt to satisfy them leads at best to "a doubtful gain in the beginning which is more than cancelled out in the end," especially let us say in the second and third phases of the treatment in the follow-up clinic or during psychoanalysis.

An interesting question which arises in connection

171

with the relationship of psychosis to psychosomatic disorders is: are psychosomatic disorders the refuge of the strong who ignore the ordinary anxieties and stresses of life and figuratively work until they drop, or are they a manifestation of the rigid and weak? This is, of course, related to the problem of how much the ordinary neurotic anxieties and defenses serve in themselves as defenses. In part, the problem is one of semantics, but I do not believe we are anywhere near the answer. Psychosomatic diseases seem to occur among all kinds of people who have made all kinds of adjustments. These range from the greatest of statesmen, writers, and even analysts to those who, by most any standard, would be regarded as ego defectives and emotionally unstable or inadequate individuals. One of the necessary risks that we must take in treating psychosomatic disease, or any nervous disorder, is that of precipitating a psychosis. In our experience, most of the psychotic-like states have been transient ones. Possibly the fact that a patient is able to develop a psychosomatic disease is indicative of a certain type of ego strength and makes for a better prognosis.

A problem that I would like to hear more about is that concerning the appearance of multiple types of psychosomatic disease in one individual. It is an oversimplification to say that chronic anxiety produces increased stress which causes the organism to break down at its constitutionally weakest part in view of the fact that different parts are affected at different periods of stress. For instance, a young man has sciatica for four years, followed by migraine headaches for two to three years, which in turn is followed by rheumatoid arthritis.

Among medical personnel overseas, many different types of psychosomatic reactions could be observed in the same individual at different periods. One, whom I remember in particular, showed wheezing and musical rales of the asthmatic type at one time. Later on, the picture changed to palmar perspiration and the appearance of small bleb-like formations in his palms with marked itching. At another time, he developed urticarial wheals, and at still another time arthriticlike pains in his neck and wrists. It is possible, of course, that psychosomatic fusions occur at various stages of libido and ego development and could be reactivated according to fluctuations in the level of regression and the nature of the aroused complex. What is certain, however, is that our knowledge is still fragmentary and our theories overly simplified.

Another problem is why patients at times do not develop a psychosomatic disease, and why psychosomatic fusions do not take place. I am treating a schizoid obsessive-compulsive man who is in the process of terminating his analysis with excellent clinical results and deep-seated personality changes, who as a baby suffered from icthyosis and "eczematoid dermatitis" up to the age of five. He has shown no skin blemishes since the age of five and did not react with his skin throughout the years of his analysis.

To recapitulate, the presence of an organic illness does not concern us as psychotherapists. Psychosomatic conditions must be treated as symbols and treated in terms of intra-ego and interpersonal relationships at all levels. The main problem from the point of view of the ego is that of strengthening its synthetic functions and

173

then weaning it. In doing so, we cannot help but partially analyze superego elements historically and mitigate their severity and rigidity. Sector therapy is accordingly much more than a verbalization technique. From the point of view of the libido theory, we preserve a positive transference, become an auxilliary ego of the patient, strengthen his control over various ego components and reduce his anxiety. In doing so, we help him to work through his problems and sharpen his perceptions and thus aid him in object satisfaction attainment.

SUMMARY

FELIX DEUTSCH, M.D.

A brief review of the highlights of this symposium and of the discussion should first refer to the areas of general agreement. We found that the application of basic psychoanalytic principles to psychosomatic disorders promises to yield fruitful data in the clinical research of these symptom complexes. Moreover, it has methodological implications for the investigation of the development and structure of these disorders, as well as a bearing on the technique and the goal of analytic therapy of these disorders.

A metapsychogical approach appears most promising if these pathological processes are studied by dissolving them into simpler components. By and large, the analytic investigation tries to clarify the meaning, the purpose, the choice, the specificity, the development, and the origin, of the symptoms. The theoretical concept is essentially that of determinism, causality, regression, and repetition compulsion.

From this concept it follows that the biologic expression of the unconscious is due to a preformed functional pattern of the past. It seems that the trigger situation of the present, which set the specific biologic function in motion, contains only some first-order components necessary for the bodily manifestation, while others may secondarily have contributed to it to a small or large degree, though not an essential one.

It has been pointed out that these manifestations derive from the stimulation of certain sensory patterns which have a well-determined preëxistent meaning in the unconscious. It may determine the specificity of the functional pattern. The more sense perceptions are involved in the trigger situation, the quicker is the psychosomatic response precipitated. Their efficacy as conditioning factors lies in a fusion and interaction of psychic and somatic phenomena which begins at a very early age, becomes solidified, and persists throughout life. It is responsible for the physiologic regression which appears simultaneously with the psychic one. This concept of the psychosomatic process invalidates the term "psychogenic," which contradicts the concept of the perpetual function of innate psychic elements under normal as well as under pathologic conditions. From the analytic point of view, all biologic functions are continually governed psychodynamically.

As to the choice of the organ system, it still holds true that the organ system involved is determined by the fact that it was the organ which was originally affected at a time antedating the full evolution of instinctual life, and, further, by a fusion of psychological and physiological processes. We cannot overstress the importance of deficient gratification in the mother-child relationship for the psychophysiologic fixation on an infantile level and for the choice of the somatic dysfunction.

This view implies that the treatment of a psychosomatic illness should restore the equilibrium at the in-

176

fantile roots; to achieve this, it must be oriented not toward the symptoms but toward their etiology. Hence, psychoanalysis or a therapy based on analytic principles seems to be the treatment of choice for psychosomatic disorders.

It is evident from the symposium and the discussion that analytic investigators are now turning their attention to basic physiologic and pathologic phenomena as well as to motor-sensory behavior patterns during the analytic session. In this way it may be possible to obtain reliable psychosomatic correlations.

INDEX

Abreaction, 105
Action pattern, 49
Adaptation, 21, 83, 156
Affect hunger, 83
Affects, 5, 10, 19, 23, 26, 33, 156-157
Aggression, 83
Alexander, F., 22, 35, 37, 39, 55, 62, 94, 95
Anaclitic depression, 10-11, 83
Anorexia, 7
Anoxia, 8
Anxiety
  and fear, 10
  theories of, 98, 146
Appendicitis, 85
Armatruda, C. A., 50, 62
Asthma, 7, 25, 43, 71-72, 87, 90, 134, 141, 164-166, 173
"Atypical" child, 93, 162
Autonomic nervous system, 65, 146, 169

Balint, M., 157
Bandler, B., 114, 141-144
Beaton, L. E., 108, 137
Benedek, T., 56, 58, 62, 82, 95
Bergler, E., 114
Bergman, P., 83, 95
Bibring, E., 114-116
Bibring, G. L., 154-157
Bichat, M. F. X., 63
Binger, C., 42, 62
Biochemistry, 63
Birth, 41, 53
Blau, A., 124
Bleuler, E., 66
Blom, G., 164
Body image, 27, 64, 142
Body-mind continuum, 26, 42
Bowel training, 15-17, 28
Brain, 26-27
  circular and reverberating circuits in, 4
  see also Central nervous system
Brodmann, K., 26

Cannon, W. B., 146
Cardiac neurosis, 29

Cardiospasm, 78
Carlson, A. G., 74
Carmichael, L., 52, 62
Castiglioni, A., 110, 136
Central nervous system, 9, 26-27, 65
Character
  defenses, 49-50
  pregenital, 68
Child, C. M., 145
Children
  analysis of, 50
  observation of, 50
  psychosis in, 83, 93
  psychosomatic diseases in, 76, 82-95
Chiropractice, 108
Coeliac disease, 86, 89, 93
Coghill, G. E., 45-46
Colic, 85, 147-148
Compulsive neurosis, 16, 69, 173
Conflict, 4, 46, 64, 80, 84, 117, 139-140
Conscious, 73, 77-78
Constipation, 15, 89, 93
Constitution, 18, 20, 86, 117, 143, 147, 153
Conversion hysteria, 7, 25, 97
Cortisone, 128
Countertransference, 127-129, 134

Dawes, L. G., 164-167
Daydream, 28
Defecation, 14-17, 31, 72
Defenses, 47, 49, 67, 78, 154
Dependency, 32, 43, 75, 78, 82-95, 154
Deutsch, F., 4, 22, 27, 35, 36, 84, 95, 130-131, 136, 148, 157-161, 170, 175-177
Diabetes, 10-11, 29-30, 87, 91
Diagnosis, 26, 34, 113-114
Diarrhea, 12, 93, 147
Dream, 28, 75-76, 79, 127
Dunbar, F., 6, 35, 39, 62, 140, 167
Duodenal ulcer, 7, 25, 87, 89-90, 93
Dysentery, 85

Eczema, 43, 87, 90, 173

179

181

2284-3-14
58